Women of Color
in STEM

A volume in
Research on Women and Education
Beverly J. Irby and Julia Ballenger, *Series Editors*
Janice Koch, *Editor Emerita*

Women of Color in STEM

Navigating the Double Bind in Higher Education

edited by

Beverly J. Irby
Texas A&M University

Nahed Abdelrahman
Texas A&M University

Barbara Polnick
Texas A&M University

Julia Ballenger
Texas A&M University–Commerce

INFORMATION AGE PUBLISHING, INC.
Charlotte, NC • www.infoagepub.com

Library of Congress Cataloging-in-Publication Data

A CIP record for this book is available from the Library of Congress
http://www.loc.gov

ISBN: 978-1-64802-369-9 (Paperback)
       978-1-64802-370-5 (Hardcover)
       978-1-64802-371-2 (E-Book)

CONTENTS

FOREWORD

Sonia J. Garcia

As I read this extraordinary book, *Women of Color in STEM: Navigating the Double Bind in Higher Education*, I truly felt as though the book was describing my own higher education experiences in its entirety. Chapter by chapter, I was mesmerized, I felt my life story was being narrated to me, from the beginning of my higher education experiences in the United States as a student all the way to my professional career in higher education. As a Latina immigrant, a woman, an administrator, a practitioner, and a lecturer, I also underwent the hardships, biases, insecurities, and double bind experiences described in this book during my own journey through higher education.

Although women have gained traction in STEM fields, Latinas and Black women still lag much further behind than any other ethnic group. Sadly, the pipeline for Black and Latina women in STEM is still very leaky and putting a mere seal on the leak will not suffice without serious, purposeful, and deliberate action. Increasing participation in STEM skills is pivotal to compete in a global economy; increasing participation of Black and Latina women among STEM is necessary to accomplish not only the national goal to prepare one million additional STEM professionals, but also, to prepare a strong national workforce. The underutilization of Black and Latina women is not only hurting the economy, but it is also keeping a group of women segregated and silenced from rich and diverse contributions to the STEM and engineering fields.

I think everyone will find this book a great resource, but especially, administrators, practitioners, faculty, and staff in higher education, as well as educators in STEM and engineering programs in the nation. Extensive qualitative data presented by the authors, obtained via interviews, be it face-to-face, groups or individuals, will be of tremendous value. Results collected show some interesting emergent themes about what currently works in higher education in order to retain and facilitate successful undergraduate degrees in STEM for Black and Latina women, as well as what needs to be fixed. Some of the elements that address gaps and barriers identified in the research are, for instance, support groups, developmental education, high impact programs, social networks, and mentoring. The information shared by the authors will benefit a range of stakeholders, such as, policy makers, educators, and program designers.

In addition to being a great resource, this book also provides inspiration—inspiration to pursue the opportunities narrated in the research to close the gaps, remove the barriers, fix the leaky talent pipeline, tap the true capabilities, and change the future for Black and Latina women. A future in which it will be normal that women of color save the day in, for instance, national space programs. History presented the resource material for a great book such as *Hidden Figures* (Shetterly, 2016), which was then adapted into a successful movie. Let this book inspire many readers to address the challenges and make the difference for a new generation that deserves support.

Here is a quick glance at the book. The authors present great compelling data support on the importance of supporting women of color navigating the challenges of higher education. Chapter 1 brings forward the voices of 21 undergraduate Black and Latina women as they share their difficulties navigating higher education with challenges based on gender and ethnicity, better known as the double bind, but they also shed light on programs that strongly supported their journey. Chapter 2 discusses the importance of social networks in exploring students' identity construction, resulting in retention and successful degree completion. Chapter 3 discusses academic resilience, risk factors or events that increase probabilities of a negative outcome, and productivity factors, positive experiences that shield individuals from negative circumstances. Chapter 4 shed light into the lives, through personal narratives, of four professional Black female professors ranging from K–12 to higher education, their common but also their individual challenges and what motivated them to persist in academia and in STEM fields. Chapter 5 highlights the journey of six Black doctoral students in STEM. This chapter explores the factors that impacted their career success as well as the commonality and individuality of their experiences. Chapter 6 focuses on Latinas in computing and how they come to see themselves, and to be seen by others as successful and empowered computer science students. The interviews revealed how Latinas negotiate disciplinary cultures that subordinate them as women and as Hispanic individuals. Chapter 7 describes the challenges of Latinas and the math performance gaps that exist between those Latinas who came to the United States as voluntary immigrants, meaning, by their own will, and those who came as involuntary immigrants. Chapter 8 presents research findings of the experiences of African American women in the world of STEM, but it focuses particularly on individual accounts of women living a life of double bind in the field of chemistry. Finally, Chapter 9 asks the difficult questions, such as, "Why aren't there more African American in STEM, and what can be done to rectify this situation?" This chapter also discusses the benefits of project-based learning (PBL).

REFERENCE

Shetterly, M. L. (2016). *Hidden figures: The American dream and the untold story of the black women mathematicians who helped win the space race.* Harper Collins.

INTRODUCTION

Beverly J. Irby
Barbara Polnick
Julia Ballenger
Nahed Abdelrahman

Though there has been a rapid increase of women's representation in law and business, their representation in STEM fields has not been matched. Researchers have revealed that there are several environmental and social barriers including stereotypes, gender bias, and the climate of science and engineering departments in colleges and universities that continue to block women's progress in STEM. In this book, the authors address the issues that encounter women of color in STEM in higher education.

In Chapter 1, Tonisha Lane and Melissa Soto emphasize that underrepresented students—especially undergraduate women of color—play a vital role in developing and sustaining a robust, U.S.-based STEM talent pool, and such students have been identified as a major source of underutilized talent in STEM. Despite this recognition, and in spite of the appreciable progress made by women in certain disciplinary STEM areas today (National Science Foundation, 2013), the number of women who are Black and Latina remain severely underrepresented. Lane and Soto captured the voices of 21 undergraduate Black women and Latinas in these fields who attribute their recent, successful pathway to their STEM degree attainment and to their participation in a STEM enrichment program.

Women of Color In STEM, pages xi–xiv
Copyright © 2021 by Information Age Publishing
All rights of reproduction in any form reserved.

In Chapter 2, Eirka Mein, Alberto Esquinca, Elsa Villa, and Angelica Monarrez, share their case study in which they explored the affordances and constraints of Latina engineering students' social networks in their academic and professional pathways as they developed as engineers. Their findings show the critical role of teacher-mentors in influencing Latina students' (a) academic and career paths, (b) familial influences, and (c) access to important apprenticeship experiences afforded by social networks.

In Chapter 3, Liza Renee Lizcano and Rosalía Chávez Zárate focused on two participants who were selected from a larger study. These participants were interviewed to examine their STEM trajectories at different time points related to challenges, achievement, self-efficacy beliefs, and contextual factors. Lizcano and Zarate focused their interview questions on exploring the participants' early STEM experiences, high school experiences in STEM, transition to college, college experiences, and their graduate school experiences. Lizcano and Zarate reported that participants struggled with diverse risk factors that impacted their self-confidence: feeling ill-prepared; having unsupportive peers and professors/advisors; feeling pressured to conform to a male-dominated environment; feeling a lack of a sense of belonging; and experiencing microaggressions, racism, and sexism.

In Chapter 4, Erika Bullock, Jacqueline Leonard, Joi Spencer, and Erica Walker shed light on their educators roles in a STEM system in higher education. Bullock et al. explored their own experiences as four Black female professors of mathematics education at different ranks and different universities. Herein, they presented counter-stories of their experiences as co-constructors of knowledge with their students. The authors examined ways to engage in deliberate discourse about race, ethnicity, gender, and class in mathematics education. Each author reflected on her experiences as a mathematics student, teacher, and teacher educator in a predominately White institution. The cross-case analyses of these counter-stories reveal opportunities and challenges for Black women whose work focuses on bringing children of color from the margins and into full participation in mathematics.

In Chapter 5, Virginia Tickles and Crystal Foxx present the experiences of six Black women holding doctorates in STEM disciplines for the purpose of exploring the factors that impacted their career success and the commonalities of their experiences. Tickles and Foxx identified that the spiritual factor as being at the core of their success. Tickles and Foxx also noted that the support of family, friends, role models, mentors, teachers, professors, and advisors was crucial to the road to success, with both negative and positive impacts. In addition, they emphasized that women's internal desires were to succeed and their self-knowledge of the environment and the opportunities that exist in the environment were vital to help avoid issues of race and gender. They also found that the desire to succeed and their self-knowledge helped to prevent an overwhelming feeling of disillusionment.

In Chapter 6, Heather Thiry and Sarah Hug focused on the experiences of Latinas within the field of computing and explored the ways in which Latina undergraduates come to see themselves, and to be seen by others, as successful and empowered computer science students. The larger purpose of the chapter was to understand how Latinas negotiated disciplinary cultures that subordinated them as women and as individuals of Hispanic origin. Through interviews with Latina computing majors, Thiry and Hug explored the constraints and affordances they encountered in authoring competent identities in technical fields. Thiry and Hug found the Latinas recounted many instances of bias and microaggressions, yet participants' shift away from isolation and marginalization was fostered by interactions with Latina role models who situated the student's negative experiences within inequitable social, cultural, and historical legacies in computing. They also noted that role models served as catalysts to transform the student's understanding of their own experiences and helped to redefine their professional identities as Latinas in computing.

In Chapter 7, Solongo Chuluunbaatar noted that while race plays an important role in the achievement gap of minority students, gender is an equally vital issue that needs to be addressed in math and science learning. She shares an interview how one African American female accomplishes her goal to get higher education by focusing on the factors that are related to the sociohistorical, community, school, and individual level. Therefore, her preliminary purpose of this interview was to find racial and gender issues related to African American women in science.

In Chapter 8, Natasha Hillsman Johnson sought an understanding of how African American female undergraduate STEM students respond to academic difficulty while enrolled in a freshman chemistry course. Johnson compared experiences of two African American female students in the chemistry program at a traditionally White institution. The research participants who shared their experiences all expressed instructional strategies, as well as the course design as being major barriers to learning chemistry. Additionally, participants identified high expectations and a value of education as contributing factors to their performance in the introductory chemistry course.

In Chapter 9, Clair Berube and Patti Horne noted that little research has been conducted to investigate the effects of problem-based learning (PBL) on both quantitative and qualitative outcomes of African American preservice science teachers. Therefore, they developed their chapter to investigate how infusing PBL into science methods courses influenced preservice science teacher self-efficacy. They conducted their chapter on the basis of the results of their previous study in which they interviewed nine African

American preservice teachers. In this chapter, the authors delved into the results of those African American participants and included qualitative data from current African American student participants to seek the answers to questions not addressed in the previous study. The authors also examined the unique problems and challenges of their current African American students who are currently enrolled in their science methods courses.

CHAPTER 1

ADVANCING BLACK FEMALE AND LATINA COLLEGIANS IN STEM

Mitigating Challenges Through STEM Enrichment Program Opportunities

Tonisha B. Lane
Melissa Soto
Kyaien O'Conner

For decades, national actors have called attention to the need for a broadened participation in undergraduate science, technology, engineering, and mathematics (STEM) as a necessity to maintain preeminence in these strategically important areas (Project Kaleidoscope 2002, 2006). Despite the United States's traditional reliance on attracting foreign-born scientists and engineers to populate its STEM workforce (National Science Board [NSB], 2010), emerging global economies and increased global competition no longer allow the United States to fully rely on this approach to contribute to our nation's economic prosperity, security, and social development.

Women of Color In STEM, pages 1–22

1

Underrepresented minority students—especially undergraduate women of color, defined as Black females and Latinas in this study—play a vital role in developing and sustaining a robust, U.S.-based STEM talent pool and have been identified as a major source of underutilized talent in these critical areas (Committee on Equal Opportunities in Science and Engineering [CEOSE], 2011). Despite this recognition and in spite of the appreciable progress made by women in certain disciplinary STEM areas today (National Science Foundation [NSF], 2013) the number of women who are Black and Latina remain severely underrepresented. Furthermore, the issue of "what works" to retain and facilitate a successful undergraduate STEM career pathway for undergraduate Black females and Latinas in STEM remains largely elusive.

In the current study, we capture the voices of 21 undergraduate Black females and Latinas in these fields who attribute their recent, successful pathway to STEM degree attainment to their participation in a STEM enrichment program. This study is important because it not only details the obstacles encountered by the participants as they seek to attain a STEM degree, it also deconstructs *how* and *why* particular STEM enrichment program components facilitate STEM degree completion for Black female and Latina collegians in STEM by examining the interplay of their institutional, environmental, and STEM enrichment program experiences.

LITERATURE REVIEW

The Status of Women of Color Collegians in STEM

Women have gained traction within the STEM fields. For instance, in 2010, 58% of bachelor's degrees awarded in the biological sciences were awarded to women (NSF, 2013). Women's share of bachelor's degrees in the physical sciences increased from 32% in 1991 to 41% in 2010 (NSF, 2013). While the latter statistic indeed reflects progress, the pace of advancement is appreciably slow given a <10% increase over a 20-year time span. What is more, upon closer examination, much work still remains if our national goal is to attract and develop a robust STEM talent pool—especially since Black females and Latinas have been identified as a major source of underutilized STEM talent that can significantly contribute to strengthen and sustain the economic vitality of the United States (CEOSE, 2011).

As of 2010, only 18% of engineering and 18% of computer science bachelor's degrees were awarded to women at-large (NSF, 2013). Of the 18% of women who attained an engineering bachelor's degree, a mere 3% were awarded to Black, Latina (and Native American) women combined (NSF, 2013). In addition, of the 18% of women who attained a computer sciences bachelor's degree, only 5% were awarded to Black, Latina (and Native American) women combined (NSF, 2013). Furthermore, while women's share of bachelor's degrees awarded in mathematics was 43% in 2010 and 41% in the physical sciences of that same year (NSF, 2013), Black, Latina (and Native American) women comprised only 5% of the degrees awarded in mathematics, and 6% of the degrees awarded in physical sciences (NSF, 2013). There are several factors that may contribute to the low representation of women of color in these fields.

Challenges

Scholars suggest that women of color often confront an uncomfortable existence with their "double-bind" status as they assert themselves in STEM fields (Ong, Wright, Espinosa, & Orfield, 2011). The double-bind construct emphasizes the difficulty of existing at the intersection of gender *and* race/ ethnicity, particularly in largely White and male dominated spaces, such as in the STEM fields. Many undergraduate STEM women of color experience difficulties establishing relationships with professors and their peers (Johnson, 2012). They often report feelings of isolation and alienation, in part, due to their inability to form study groups when other women of color are not present (Ong et al., 2011). Additionally, relationship building with faculty may be exacerbated due to their perceived interests in relaying subject content over developing relationships with their students (Johnson, 2007). These circumstances contribute to the barriers women of color face when seeking out a community in the STEM disciplines.

Developmental Education

Insufficient access to academic resources often increases the need for developmental education, especially for minorities and low-income students (Pascarella & Terenzini, 2005). In a quantitative study investigating freshmen enrolled in California's community colleges, Bahr (2010) discovered that Blacks and Hispanics were overly represented in developmental mathematics. Fortunately, studies show that participation in developmental mathematics can help students strengthen their math skills and persist in STEM majors (Bahr, 2010; Crisp, Nora, & Taggart, 2009). When remediation is properly executed, Black students persist at the same rate as their non-Black peers (Bahr, 2010). In another study examining the outcomes of Hispanic students, results revealed that these students were not hindered by their start in developmental math courses, in most cases, they graduated with STEM degrees (Crisp et al., 2009). While there are mixed reviews on the outcomes of STEM students of color who participate in developmental mathematics courses, evidence also points to its potential.

Sense of Belonging

Scholars assert that a sense of belonging contributes to positive academic and social outcomes (Hausmann, Ye, Schofield, & Woods, 2009; Locks, Hurtado, Bowman, & Oseguera, 2008). Central to the present study, having a sense of belonging is increasingly recognized as critical to the success of STEM students. Belonging experiences play a significant role in the decision for STEM students to persist or leave the major (Seymour & Hewitt, 1997; Strayhorn, 2012). For example, Strayhorn (2012) uncovered that underrepresented STEM students who lacked a sense of belonging also experienced diminished identities, self-esteem, and confidence to pursue STEM. In contrast, students who frequently interacted with diverse peers expressed higher levels of self-esteem (Strayhorn, 2008a). In another study, Strayhorn (2012) concluded that students who engaged in an undergraduate research program had a greater sense of belonging at the conclusion of the program. Sense of belonging was also found to have a positive relationship with intersectionality, suggesting that a student's multiple identities may affect his or her connection to a community (Strayhorn, 2008b). Thus, one's gender and race may also influence belonging experiences or lack thereof for STEM students and undergraduate women of color specifically.

Establishing a Science Identity

The emergent research shows a relationship between having a salient science identity and student success (Chang, Eagan, Lin, & Hurtado, 2011; Eagan et al., 2013). In fact, a growing number of studies acknowledge that participation in undergraduate research reinforces commitment to and persistence within STEM (Carter, Mandell, & Maton, 2009; Eagan et al., 2013; Hurtado, Cabrera, Lin, Arellano, & Espinosa, 2009). Slovacek, Whittinghill, Flenoury, and Wiseman (2012) investigated the outcomes of two cohorts of participants in the National Institute of Health's (NIH) Minority Opportunities in Research (MORE) program. Students who participated in the MORE program had higher GPAs, took less time to earn their degrees, were more likely to earn a STEM degree, and pursued graduate degrees at higher rates than nonparticipants. Slovacek and colleagues (2012) concluded that engaging in research provided opportunities for them to "think as scientists" and to "acculturate into the larger scientific community" (p. 214). In another study, Lu (2013) found that Latino males involved in a designated scientific community perceived themselves as scientists, sustained their interest in STEM, and felt more connected to their major compared to Latino males who were not a part of this scientific community. In contrast, Latino males who were not a part of this scientific community questioned their existence in a STEM major or failed to have social interactions with other STEM students (Lu, 2013). These insights should also be considered when examining factors that may facilitate or impede the educational advancement of undergraduate Black females and Latinas in STEM.

STEM Enrichment Programs

In the 1970s, minority program offices were established in natural science and engineering colleges to provide opportunities for minority students to transition into and succeed in the STEM fields (Shehab, Murphy, & Foor, 2012). Over time, structured programming including academic advising, mentoring, and tutoring was implemented to reduce attrition among students of color (Tsui, 2007). Moreover, the extant literature shows that students who participate in STEM enrichment programs experience smoother transitions into higher education (Johnson, 2012), better psychosocial adjustment (Shehab et al., 2012), and academic success (Treisman, 1992).

Given the important role that STEM enrichment programs play, there is a need for additional empirical studies that address the impact of these programs on the experiences and outcomes of students of color (Museus, Palmer, Davis, & Maramba, 2011). Much of the literature on these programs exists in reports and nonacademic publications which lack a theoretical basis and rigorous research methods. Additionally, many of the current studies about STEM enrichment programs focus on describing the program (Palmer, Maramba, & Dancy, 2013), using quantitative methods (Pender, Marcotte, Sto. Domingo, & Maton, 2010), and discussing program outcomes of all participants (Carter et al., 2009). These studies fail to delineate the experiences of Black females and Latinas and how these programs contribute to their success. Such findings may help with establishing best practices and replication of services at other institutions.

CONCEPTUAL FRAMEWORK

This study utilized an integrated theoretical framework using the following: (a) the Expertise Model of Student Success (EMSS), (b) sense of belonging, and (c) science identity development. EMSS was derived from the work of Padilla (2009), who suggested that successful students overcome barriers in college settings from acquiring academic (i.e., disciplinary-specific) and heuristic (i.e., context-specific) knowledge. This knowledge attainment leads to purposeful action that facilitates persistence and subsequent degree attainment.

The second theoretical lens used in this study is sense of belonging. According to Strayhorn (2012), "Sense of belonging refers to a students' perceived social support on campus, a feeling or sensation of connectedness, the experience of mattering or feeling cared about, accepted, respected, valued by, and important to the group (e.g., campus community) or others on campus (e.g., faculty, peers)" (p. 3). This lens was used to analyze data that suggested an emotional connection to an environment and to the people within it that led to forms of individual motivation to pursue purposeful actions. In a college setting, these actions may include studying and attending class regularly, and outcomes may include earning good grades and persisting in college.

The third construct is based on the emerging body of work that points to science identity development as an important factor for student retention and persistence. One's science identity is achieved through opportunities to *perform* in science contexts, to demonstrate *competence*, and to experience *recognition* (Carlone & Johnson, 2007). This integrated model was used as a framework to investigate the perceptions and experiences of Black females and Latina collegians in a STEM enrichment program at a predominantly White, public research university.

METHOD

The current study is a part of a larger case study in which we examined a STEM enrichment program designed to facilitate academic readiness and psychosocial adjustment among students of color in the STEM fields. The purpose of the current study was to (a) identify factors that create challenges for Black females and Latinas in the STEM fields, and (b) ascertain how a STEM enrichment program provides opportunities that facilitate successful pathways for this group. Data generated from document analyses, observations, and semi-structured and focus group interviews from 21 Black female and Latina program participants and recent baccalaureate recipients informed this chapter.

This study took place at Jefferson State University (JSU; pseudonym), a predominantly White, large, public research university in the Midwest (PWI). Each year at JSU, approximately 10% of the students pursuing degrees in STEM are students of color. Yet, there is a 20% graduation gap between students of color and their White counterparts in these disciplines. At JSU, a disproportionate number of students of color begin their college careers in math courses below calculus. Based on institutional data analytics, calculus has a strong predictive relationship to earning a STEM degree.

The Comprehensive STEM Program (CSP, pseudonym), a STEM enrichment program at JSU, was established in 2007 with the National Science Foundation's Louis Stokes Alliance for Minority Participation (LSAMP) grant to acclimate first-year students to the rigorous academic culture and college life in the STEM disciplines. CSP contains eight program components: summer bridge program, residential housing, tailored university math courses, weekly recitation sessions, peer mentoring, academic advising, freshman seminar, and an undergraduate research experience. The program capacity is 50 students.

CSP was purposively selected because of its mission to support underserved students pursuing STEM degrees. A significant number of the Black and Latino students that attend JSU are from neighboring urban K–12 districts that are under-resourced. Some of the regional high schools have a less than 50% graduation rate, and few students matriculate to college. Thus, the program director of CSP developed an enrichment program that could ensure the academic readiness of students pursuing degrees in STEM.

DATA COLLECTION AND ANALYSES

Current CSP participants and recent baccalaureate recipients completed a one hour focus group interview, or, a one-on-one semi-structured interview depending on their availability (Hesse-Biber, 2010). Focus groups and one-on-one interviews were recorded, transcribed verbatim, and coded. To derive the themes, we used a pattern matching technique to code the data (Yin, 2003). Pattern matching analysis allowed us to match the interview data to the concepts embedded within the theoretical framework. We used triangulation to strengthen the trustworthiness of the study's findings in the form of multiple sources of data and peer review (Merriam, 2009). Focus groups and semi-structured interviews were used to compare and corroborate information revealed throughout the data collection process. Researcher memos from observations of program activities (i.e., summer bridge program, recitation, staff meetings), printed materials, and websites were used to understand the program and institutional contexts.

LIMITATIONS

The qualitative methodology limits the generalizability of this study, though generalizability is not and was not the point of this qualitative study. While this study closely aligns with literature regarding the experiences and perceptions of people of color and women in STEM, these findings will need to be confirmed through additional studies. Additionally, despite efforts to recruit a diverse representation of women of color in STEM, there were a relatively small number of Latina participants (5) versus Black participants (16).

FINDINGS

Black female and Latina collegians in CSP at JSU differed in their experiences in the STEM disciplines. Both groups noticed there were few women and people of color, but their responses to these circumstances were dissimilar. Whereas several of the Black women experienced a variety of hardships to obtain relevancy and support in their academic programs, the Latinas indicated pride or ambivalence about the lack of diversity or inclusivity in STEM contexts. In this study, Latinas were also more likely to be college ready and confident about their academic abilities compared to the Black female participants.

There was a high level of agreement about the opportunities CSP provided to ensure student success. CSP employed a variety of strategies and practices that facilitate student success for Black female and Latina students in STEM including addressing academic knowledge gaps, strengthening their science identity, and building relationships. Findings also indicated that students who had engaged in undergraduate research were more likely to possess a strong science identity compared to program participants who had not engaged in undergraduate research.

Overview of Challenges

In this study, three themes emerged that posed barriers for Black female and Latina participants as they each set a path to pursue a STEM degree. First, due to their precollege educational contexts, the Black participants were more likely to feel less prepared and confident to perform academically compared to the Latinas. Second, the participants discussed the lack of diversity among the students and faculty in the STEM disciplines. Third, the Black women were concerned about the messaging they received about the aptitude of women and people of color. Using the voices of the women, these challenges are discussed further below.

Developmental Math Starters

A significant number of students of color are placed into developmental mathematics at JSU. Specifically, approximately 10% of JSU students interested in earning a STEM degree begin in developmental mathematics. Due to their low persistence and retention rates, administrators often emphasize that developmental math starters should change their major early in their college careers. For instance, Monet recounted:

> I remember one of the associate deans told us if we started off in [developmental mathematics or college algebra] we're never gonna be engineers. [But] most Black people start here [and, if] you're not going to be able to finish you might as well stop now. I don't understand what benefits you for saying that to me. What benefits you for oppressing us still, because we're trying to better our lives? Like . . . that makes me upset. It makes me so mad because it's just so messed up.

Monet identified placing into developmental mathematics as a form of oppression. The associate dean's remarks about an inability of developmental math starters to succeed in engineering added to her feeling of oppression. Given that CSP is designed to facilitate college readiness for underserved students, the associate dean's assertion that these students would be unable to succeed is ironic.

"There Are No women"

Many of the Black female and Latina STEM participants expressed their discontent that there were few female students of color in their classes. Some women also discussed how male peers were reluctant to help them. For instance, Brittney stated:

> The second thing that's difficult as you matriculate [through] your classes [is] there are no women. The guys, they don't feel like they should help you so it's just like you're by yourself. And there's only like two or three Black people in all my classes and I have a class where I'm the only girl and the only Black person . . . [it's] just a whole different vibe.

For Brittney, the lack of critical mass of women and Blacks makes the classroom feel isolating and alienating. She even lamented that there is a "whole different vibe" suggesting that the culture and climate is different than other contexts she may be involved with as a student. Many participants acknowledged that there were little to no women or people of color in their classroom settings. They even noted the pervasiveness of Whiteness, and how they noticeably stood out in the classroom. Jackie described the experience of being the "only Black girl" as a "weird" and "funny feeling." Institutions with large proportions of White students minimize opportunities for students to interact with individuals from other racial and ethnic groups, promote tokenism, and reinforce stereotypes (Hurtado, Clayton-Pedersen, Allen, & Milem, 1998).

Being a Black Female in STEM Is Hard

Monet described her experiences in STEM as "hard." Though she appreciated the help and support her faculty member gave her, she was more likely—in comparison to her majority peers—to be questioned about various content areas in lectures:

> I was the only Black female in a couple of my chemical engineering classes at State and it was really discouraging because if you ask a question or you ask for help, they'll give you that side eye, like do you really know what you're talking about. [But] I can bring something to the table ... it was good and bad. One, it was good because the professor always knew who I was and he always made sure that I understood the problems and the different situations that were going on in class, [and he] made sure that I comprehended it all. But it also was like why you gotta pinpoint me out? That's how you feel, like why you gotta ask me? Why don't you ask the other people? So ... being a Black female in STEM is really hard, flat out, because I just feel like you always have to make sure you're on top of your game and always just ahead, ahead of the curve, because if you fall behind, I feel like you won't have the support to bring you back.

Monet described the hardships of minoritized status in a PWI. Though she had a professor that ensured she understood the course material, she experienced a heightened sensitivity to being identified in the classroom. She also felt the pressures of the double bind; she often talked about needing to prove herself or stay "on top of her game." When students are the sole representation of their race and gender, they may feel compelled to overcompensate to disprove the stereotypes held about their social identity groups.

"They Think We Don't Know Anything"

Several students discussed how White male students believed women of color were less intelligent or had less to contribute to course projects. When we asked students if they were treated differently because of their race and gender, most students responded in the affirmative. The Latina participants and a Black woman stated that they did not experience differential treatment, or they did not allow the actions of their peers to affect them. Brittney communicated through examples and nonverbal expression (i.e., gestures, intonation, and inflection) the extent to which the actions and behaviors of her peers affected her academic experiences:

> **Brittney:** They just think that we don't know anything. Like we don't know what's going on in the class. [Or], they automatically do not form a conversation or form a group with [you], [because they think] the Black people don't know what's going on or they just here . . . especially with girls. They don't want you to . . . see you like doing better. I had five exams last week. And people [were] like, even some of my Black [guy] friends [asked] what'd you get on your exam? They'd be like oh, no, you didn't. Or they might know an equation that you can put on a [formula] sheet. They won't tell you. They just wanta see you struggle.
>
> **Interviewer:** Why do you think that is?
>
> **Brittney:** I think people don't wanta see women succeed in life. [For example], in my 400-level design class we had to write about where we plan to work after graduation. I had to give mine . . . and they said, the only reason, you're working at General Motors [is because] they got a woman CEO now. Like dang, [this opportunity] happened before that.

Brittney indicates several micro- and macro-level challenges to the state of women in STEM. In general, she believes that people do not want women to succeed. She suggests that White male peers are less likely to converse with or form groups with women of color, they are less likely to share study aids, and they are more likely to believe that women of color benefit from preferential treatment. These kinds of experiences contribute to the arduous process of earning a STEM degree. The STEM disciplines require a great deal of collaboration, cooperation and interdependence (Seymour & Hewitt, 1997). The inability to interact with peers across racial differences could lead to academic underperformance or incomplete tasks. Dealing with such frustrations can be daunting, especially when one is undergoing identity development and seeking relevancy in a hegemonic context. Without the appropriate support to circumvent these challenges, women of color may be less likely to persist.

Opportunities

CSP offers a myriad of opportunities for students to be affirmed and counteract some of the hardships faced by program participants within the larger university and as a result of systemic opportunity gaps. Marks defined the opportunity gap as "a failure to provide the resources and exposure students need to be successful" (as cited in Arnett, 2014, para. 4). Enabling students to improve their cognitive skills, engage in undergraduate research, and develop relationships contributes to their successful outcomes. Findings revealed three recurrent themes that were key opportunities afforded to Black female and Latina STEM undergraduate participants through CSP: two were program components (i.e., recitation, undergraduate research experience) and one was a program outcome (i.e., relationship building).

Recitation

Many of the participants commented on the support rendered through recitation. The mandatory recitation sessions occur on a weekly basis, Monday through Thursday from 7:00 p.m.–9:30 p.m. Students appreciate the consistency and structure of recitation. For instance, Amanda stated that it helped her to be "more disciplined." She even pointed out that she would probably be "behind on like a lot of my homework and studying" if not for the structure of the recitation. Autumn discussed the importance of having a "controlled space" and "designated time" in which to study. Emily contended that recitation allowed her to teach other students, which is important to her academic development:

> Actually, it helps me in a different kind of way. I don't necessarily get all my work done here, but I do get some questions answered. But I like helping other people and that helps me understand my work better. So just having a group of students that will ask me questions rather than some of my [other science college] friends, who we work and study together, but it's different. Like we're studying together and I'm not really answering their questions. But coming to recitation, I get to answer people's questions and then I learn more from that.

Recitation provides opportunities for students to study with peers in similar majors. The students share information, resources, and academic knowledge in subject areas. For instance, Autumn discussed how she appreciated establishing study groups with CSP participants who were also enrolled in her classes. Additionally, she stated, "I mean, the way, we all do homework together so if there's one person who knows how to do one problem, that person explains it to the entire group."

CSP lends itself to a community of mutual reciprocity such that members of the group are both learners and teachers. This behavior counters the dominant competitive culture in STEM. For example, Emily acknowledged that her other science college friends, who are not a part of CSP, do not ask very many questions in their study groups because it is a perception that one should already know the answer if one is to be competitive for entry into medical school. In contrast, the CSP group was "not afraid to ask or answer questions," and she valued that aspect of the community.

"The Summer Bridge Program Is Really a Bridge"

The participants described the summer bridge program as an actual bridge to the first year in college. They discussed how it provided an "extra boost," "prepared" students, and helped students to identify and overcome gaps in their math knowledge. For example, Amanda described the quasi-college nature of the program:

> During the summer program, it was pretty much run like college. We were treated as college [students]. We had more responsibility so we learned like to think more . . . as an adult as far as like being dependent [of] having somebody else to tell us when to do something or when to wake up. We had to do it on our own. Also, just knowing the campus and knowing how to get around. I think that helped out a lot . . . and knowing people. We met more people so we weren't alone.

Amanda pointed out that participating in the summer bridge helped students to think and act like adults. Due to phenomena such as helicopter parenting and the highly structured lives of adolescents (Padilla-Walker & Nelson, 2012), many students are not accustomed to making their own decisions or being independent. As the CSP director often says, the students were in high school just 3 months ago. For some students, it is quite difficult to transition from thinking like a high school student to a college student.

Another critical feature of the summer bridge program is the math course. At the beginning of the program, students are given a CSP designed assessment. This assessment differs from the university's placement exam. The program instructors believe their assessment is a better predictor of students' actual math abilities. Autumn explained this approach in the following quote:

> We took a pretest, and then they broke the [math] classes up based on whether or not you needed help in trigonometry and [or] in algebra. It seemed like everyone was struggling but that's because they put you in the class for what you needed help with and not for the one that you knew the most about.

This approach appeared to work as evidenced by the scores students earned on the second university math placement exams taken at the conclusion of the program. In 2012, 88% of students improved their math scores, and in 2013, 94% of the participants increased their math scores.

Participating in the summer bridge program also prepares students for the expectations of college level work and allows students to identify study partners. Legacy noted:

> The work was so much harder [in CSP] but I loved it because it prepare[d] me, it set my standards so high for college that now, I'm still working at a [CSP] standard and [non-participants are] working at a freshman year college [standard]. If I didn't have people that I study with in ESSA for the first semester, I probably would've been by myself, trying to figure out [the material]. I feel like actually having somebody you know, somebody you can see walking down [University] Road, like hey, what you doing, it's like actually knowing somebody [is] there for you. Meeting people and having someone that you can walk by and see, it's a real good feeling.

Due to the strategies and approaches applied in the summer bridge program, Legacy felt more prepared for her first year in college. She even conjectured that students who did not have a summer bridge experience were operating at a standard lower than she. She also credited the program with helping her to identify people to study with. Without the program, she believed she would have been alone with little academic support. Lastly, Legacy acknowledged an emotional connection to her ability to see people she knew throughout the campus environment when she stated "it's like a real good feeling." The literature speaks to the importance of having a sense of belonging for marginalized groups such as those who are first-generation college students, lower-income students, students of color, and women in STEM (Strayhorn, 2012). Legacy fits into all of these social identities, making it even more necessary for Legacy's persistence to feel acceptance in the JSU community.

Undergraduate Research Experiences

In the current study, the participants had overwhelmingly positive outcomes with their undergraduate research experiences. According to Carlone and Johnson (2007), opportunities to perform scientific practices, gain competencies, and earn recognition are critical components to developing a strong science identity. Students who engaged in undergraduate research exhibited stronger science identities than students who did not. The hands-on experiences, opportunities to develop relationships with faculty members, and learning that they were capable of doing relevant scientific work seemed to influence their science identity. For instance, Jasmine emphasized how she appreciated "doing stuff" and "not just reading books."

Storm explained various meaningful aspects that were involved in her undergraduate research experience:

> Well, we had [lab] meetings every Wednesday at 8 in the morning, and he invited me to those so that was really cool. The grad students [enhanced my undergraduate research experiences], too. There was one grad student who I worked with a lot. She gave me a bunch of readings, like articles, and then she gave me a big grad book and some type of electrical engineering [book]. She made me do problems that [were] kind of difficult. But I did them all right...that was a good sign. [I] worked with [the graduate student] every day, Monday through Friday, at least four hours, making the solutions. Then, I had to make a video [about making] particles, because the professor had asked me [to] make this video for future people who might come to the lab to work. So, I worked with another graduate student on that video. He was from Russia [and] also working towards his PhD in chemical engineering. I got to see how rigorous grad school can be, and [I discovered] this takes a lot of work. Then the professor...he really liked my work so he invited me to dinner at his house.

Storm experienced several advantages to engaging in research. She learned the extent and magnitude of graduate-level work and that she was capable of performing academic tasks at the graduate level. She collaborated with engineers from diverse ethnic backgrounds. Lastly, the quality of her work led to an invitation to have dinner at her faculty mentor's home. Throughout Storm's interview, she exuded how excited she was to have had these opportunities. She also discussed how this experience strengthened her confidence and certainty that she was an engineer. These kinds of experiences can be instrumental in counteracting the gendered racism some women of color encounter in the classroom. Though Storm did not recall experiencing gendered racism, many of her peers in this study did. Participating in environments, such as undergraduate research contexts, where they are affirmed and included is a precursor to establishing a strong science identity (Carlone & Johnson, 2007).

Building Critical Relationships

Black female and Latina collegians described the kinds of relationships they were able to develop through CSP. Peer mentors served as critical sources of information for navigating the university and acclimating to the academic culture of the STEM disciplines. Additionally, faculty mentors— from the undergraduate research programs—made themselves available to students thereby making them feel they were important.

Peer Mentors

Black female and Latina collegians appeared to benefit significantly from mentorship and participation in the National Society of Black Engineers (NSBE). Since the CSP director serves as the NSBE advisor, the program provides a gateway to this student organization. At the time of this study, several of the participants were a part of NSBE's all-female executive board or recently elected officials for the following academic year. Many of the NSBE members serve as resident mentors during the summer bridge program and peer mentors during the academic year. Monet shared her experience with a NSBE mentor:

> Well, one of my mentors was Melinda Smith. She was an electrical engineering major, and she was in NSBE. She became my mentor my second semester [of] freshman year. She was the main person who was always telling me you're gonna be the only one in your class and make sure you know your stuff. So, it was her and the older NSBE students [who had] been through everything that we were about to go through in the College of Engineering and Computer Science...They had so much knowledge when it [came] to tests and stuff. This is a class you probably should take, just little guidance like that and then having Melinda being 1-on-1 guide as a female, as an African American female, so I [had] somebody. If I have any questions, just somebody to talk to.

Harper (2010) contended that more researchers should investigate the value of peers for students pursuing STEM degrees. As illustrated in Monet's quote, peer mentors play an integral role in CSP and shape the college experience for women of color in STEM. Melinda was a role model for Monet, and amidst an environment with so little women, Melinda inspired and motivated Monet to persist. Additionally, having someone to talk to and confide helped Monet to feel less alienated in a PWI.

Faculty

Several students were able to cultivate relationships with faculty during their undergraduate research experiences. These encounters also allowed them to earn the respect of their faculty mentors. These relationships served them in other contexts beyond the undergraduate research experience. Jasmine provided the following example:

> I realize the importance of like making relationships with the professors. Dr. Clark, she actually came to lecture to our class on Friday and, I was able to go speak to her again but then Dr. Wilson is our professor, so then he saw that, I was more involved in different activities at JSU and then he's also seen me at like different award ceremonies. I guess just getting that spotlight [from] important professionals in the field.

Jasmine suggested that her relationship with Dr. Clark provided her a "spotlight" that garnered the respect of her current faculty member, who was also an associate dean. Faculty members were also more likely to invest time in their protégés if they were producing quality work in accordance with their standards. For instance, Sandy interacted often with her faculty mentor:

> Sandy: She was always there and we'd have meetings as a whole lab. [Then] we went to a barbecue at her house and bunch of fun stuff like that. [Also], she was in her office, if I needed help with a presentation or poster...she was there.

Sandy's faculty mentor provided scholarly and social support to her. Being available, inviting Sandy to her home, and assisting Sandy with her presentation contributed to her positive experience with research and solidified a bond.

DISCUSSION

Several conclusions may be drawn from this study. First, the findings revealed that gendered racism affects the interactions of women of color with their White, male peers in classroom environments. Prior research illuminates the unique hardships that women of color face proving their value and intelligence in the STEM disciplines (Carlone & Johnson 2007, Ong et al., 2011). These experiences contribute to the alienation and isolation some women of color endure in PWIs.

Second, despite efforts to increase women and faculty of color in STEM, they continue to be underrepresented, especially at predominantly White research universities (Bilimoria & Liang, 2011). Similar to the experiences of students of color, women and faculty of color often have to prove themselves to their colleagues and students in addition to undergoing the arduous process of earning tenure (Nelson & Rogers, 2003). These circumstances influence the shortage of diverse faculty. Consequently, female students of color have to navigate a perceivably hostile environment and negotiate their identities without women faculty role models who represent their sex and race.

Third, academic under-preparation exacerbates the minoritized status of women of color. Though academic under-preparedness is not unique to the educational experiences of communities of color, they are often outperformed by their majority peers on standardized tests. For instance, a 2012 ACT report noted that only 25% of all high school graduates met college readiness benchmarks in all four subjects (i.e., English, reading, mathematics, and science). Blacks were least likely to be college ready; only 5% met all four benchmarks. Unfortunately, students of color disproportionately attend secondary schools that are under-resourced (Palmer, Davis, Moore, & Hilton, 2010). Such experiences make it difficult to transition into a rigorous postsecondary STEM curriculum and find community in a competitive environment that ostracizes under-prepared students.

Fourth, the findings illustrate the important role that CSP plays in the persistence of Black females and Latinas in STEM. For instance, program components such as summer bridge programs and academic support increase the likelihood of success for collegians of color. This finding adds to the extant literature on the academic and psychosocial benefits of participating in STEM enrichment programs. Moreover, research shows that students of color who participate in STEM enrichment programs academically outperform nonparticipants (Treisman, 1992), express a stronger commitment to the STEM disciplines, and pursue graduate education at a greater rate (Maton, Pollard, McDougall, & Hrabowski, 2012).

Fifth, undergraduate research experiences serve multiple purposes for women of color, such as providing opportunities for recognition and demonstrating their competence. In the current study, the participants were able to engage in various meaningful activities that built their scientific skills and confidence. Unlike the classroom environment, which provided more theory-based content, students obtained hands-on experiences in research environments (Hurtado et al., 2013). Thus, increasing the number of opportunities Black female and Latina collegians have to apply their knowledge may also result in greater retention and degree attainment.

Lastly, the relationships the participants built with their peers and faculty mentors were instrumental in helping them feel like they belonged, which was dissimilar to their experiences in the classroom. This finding is not novel, but it does confirm that relationship building remains a consistent vital factor for STEM student success (Strayhorn, 2012). In the current study, Black female and Latina collegians leverage their relationships to gather critical information, earn respect, and feel valuable.

IMPLICATIONS FOR POLICY AND PRACTICE

Financial resources from institutions and external agencies are necessary for the development and sustainability of STEM enrichment programs. The program discussed in the current study was made possible by resources from the National Science Foundation and supplemented by the university's Equity and Inclusion Office and corporate sponsorship. Since grant funding is cyclical, changes in legislation may disrupt the efforts being made through these programs. Thus, colleges and universities should seek to institutionalize these programs and, perhaps, use government funding to scale these programs. Additionally, external agencies should provide designated funds for assessment and evaluation in their grants. There are hundreds of programs in the United States that have successful student outcomes, but they lack the resources to demonstrate their outcomes with quantitative data. Many of the program administrators—though highly skilled practitioners—do not have the skills to conduct their own assessment. Further, much of the financial resources allocated to these programs are used toward the direct costs of the program.

STEM enrichment program administrators should apply a multi-pronged approach to student retention and success. With the growing number of students lacking college readiness, summer bridge programs are critical to addressing academic knowledge gaps prior to the start of a student's college career. Likewise, programs should provide undergraduate research opportunities. An emergent body of scholarship suggests that student engagement in undergraduate research may be the key to strengthening commitment to STEM majors and careers (Carter et al., 2009; Eagan et al., 2013).

REFERENCES

Arnett, A. A. (2014, October 5). Experts: "Opportunity gap" key impediment to Black male academic achievement. *Diverse Issues in Higher Education.* Retrieved from https://diverseeducation.com/article/67214/

Bahr, P. R. (2010). Preparing the underprepared: An analysis of racial disparities in postsecondary mathematics remediation. *The Journal of Higher Education, 81*(2), 209–237.

Bilimoria, D., & Liang, X. (2011). *Gender equity in science and engineering: Advancing change in higher education.* New York, NY: Routledge.

Carlone, H. B., & Johnson, A. (2007). Understanding the science experiences of successful women of color: Science identity as an analytic lens. *Journal of Research in Science Teaching, 44*(8), 1187–1218.

Carter, F., Mandell, M., & Maton, K.I. (2009). The influence of on-campus, academic year undergraduate research on STEM PhD outcomes: Evidence from the Meyerhoff Scholarship Program. *Educational Evaluation and Policy Analysis, 31*(4), 441–462.

Chang, M. J., Eagan, M. K., Lin, M. H., & Hurtado, S. (2011). Considering the impact of racial stigmas and science identity: Persistence among biomedical and behavioral science aspirants. *The Journal of higher education, 82*(5), 564–596.

Committee on Equal Opportunities in Science and Engineering. (2011). *2009–2010 biennial report to congress: Broadening participation in America's STEM workforce.* Retrieved from http://www.nsf.gov/od/oia/activities/ceose/reports/2009-2010_CEOSEBiennialReportToCongress.pdf

Crisp, G., Nora, A., & Taggart, A. (2009). Student characteristics, pre-college, college, and environmental factors as predictors of majoring in and earning a

STEM degree: An analysis of students attending a Hispanic Serving Institution. *American Educational Research Journal, 46*(4), 924–942.

Eagan, M. K., Jr., Hurtado, S., Chang, M. J., Garcia, G. A., Herrera, F. A., & Garibay, J. C. (2013). Making a difference in science education: The impact of undergraduate research programs. *American educational research journal, 50*(4), 683–713.

Harper, S. R. (2010). An anti-deficit achievement framework for research on students of color in STEM. In S. R. Harper & C. B. Neman (Eds.), *Students of color in STEM: New directions for institutional research* (No. 148; pp. 63–64). San Francisco, CA: Jossey-Bass.

Hausmann, L. R., Ye, F., Schofield, J. W., & Woods, R. L. (2009). Sense of belonging and Persistence in White and African American first-year students. *Research in Higher Education, 50*(7), 649–669.

Hesse-Biber, S. (2010). Qualitative approaches to mixed methods practice. *Qualitative Inquiry, 16*(6), 455–468. *Review of Higher Education, 80*(4), 389–414.

Hurtado, S., Clayton-Pedersen, A. R., Allen, W. R., & Milem, J. F. (1998). Enhancing campus climates for racial/ethnic diversity: Educational policy and practice. *The Review of Higher Education, 21*(3), 279–302.

Hurtado, S., Cabrera, N. L., Lin, M. H., Arellano, L., & Espinosa, L. L. (2009). Diversifying science: Underrepresented student experiences in structured research programs. *Research in Higher Education, 50*(2), 189–214.

Johnson, A. C. (2007). Unintended consequences: How science professors discourage women of color. *Science Education, 91*(5), 805–821.

Johnson, D. R. (2012). Campus racial climate perceptions and overall sense of belonging among racially diverse women in STEM majors. *Journal of College Student Development, 53*(2), 336–346.

Locks, A. M., Hurtado, S., Bowman, N. A., & Oseguera, L. (2008). Extending notions of campus climate and diversity to students' transition to college. *The Review of Higher Education, 31*(3), 257–285.

Lu, C. (2013, November). *Competition, companionship, and (in)completion: A phenomenological study examining in the first semester of Latino males in STEM disciplines.* Paper presented at the 2013 Annual Association for the Study of Higher Education Conference, St. Louis, MO.

Maton, K. I., Pollard, S. A., McDougall Weise, T. V., & Hrabowski, F. A. (2012). Meyerhoff Scholars Program: A strengths-based, institution-wide approach to increasing diversity in science, technology, engineering, and mathematics. *Mount Sinai Journal of Medicine: A Journal of Translational and Personalized Medicine, 79*(5), 610–623.

Merriam, S. B. (2009). *Qualitative research: A guide to design and implementation.* San Francisco, CA: Wiley.

Museus, S. D., Palmer, R., Davis, R. J., & Maramba, D. C. (2011). *Racial and ethnic minority students' success in STEM Education. ASHE-ERIC Monograph Series.* San Francisco, CA: Jossey-Bass.

Nelson, D. J., & Rogers, D. C. (2003). *A national analysis of diversity in science and engineering faculties at research universities.* Retrieved from http://drdonnajnelson .oucreate.com//diversity/briefings/Diversity%20Report%20Final.pdf

National Science Board. (2010). *Science and engineering indicators 2010-digest.* Arlington, VA: National Science Foundation. (NSB 10-02)

National Science Foundation. (2013). *Women, minorities, and persons with disabilities in science and engineering: 2013* (Report NSF13-304). Washington, DC: Author. Retrieved from http://www.nsf.gov/statistics/wmpd/2013/pdf/nsf13304_full .pdf

Ong, M., Wright, C., Espinosa, L. L., & Orfield, G. (2011). Inside the double bind: A synthesis of empirical research on undergraduate and graduate women of color in science, technology, engineering, and mathematics. *Harvard Educational Review, 81*(2), 172–208.

Padilla, R. V. (2009). *Student success modeling: Elementary school to college.* Sterling, VA: Stylus.

Padilla-Walker, L. M., & Nelson, L. J. (2012). Black hawk down? Establishing helicopter parenting as a distinct construct from other forms of parental control during emerging adulthood. *Journal of adolescence, 35*(5), 1177–1190.

Palmer, R. T., Davis, R. J., Moore, J. L., III, & Hilton, A. A. (2010). A nation at risk: Increasing college participation and persistence among African American males to stimulate us global competitiveness. *Journal of African American Males in Education, 1*(2), 105–124.

Palmer, R. T., Maramba, D. C., & Dancy, T. E. (2013). The magnificent "MILE": Impacting Black male retention and persistence at an HBCU. *Journal of College Student Retention, 15*(1), 65–72.

Pascarella, E. T., & Terenzini, P. T. (2005). *How college affects students: A third decade of research.* San Francisco, CA: Jossey-Bass.

Pender, M., Marcotte, D. E., Sto. Domingo, M. R. S., & Maton, K. I. (2010). The STEM pipeline: The role of summer research experience in minority students' Ph.D. aspirations. *Education Policy Analysis Archives, 18*(30), 1–36.

Project Kaleidoscope. (2002). *Report on reports I: Recommendations for action in support of undergraduate science, technology, engineering, and mathematics.* Retrieved from https://www.nigms.nih.gov/training/reports/Documents/2006Report OnReports.pdf

Project Kaleidoscope. (2006). *Report on reports II: Recommendations for urgent action, transforming america's scientific and technological infrastructure.* Washington, DC: Author. Retrieved from https://www.nigms.nih.gov/training/reports/ Documents/2006ReportOnReports.pdf

Seymour, E., & Hewitt, N. M. (1997). *Talking about leaving: Why undergraduates leave the sciences.* Boulder, CO: Westview Press.

Shehab, R., Murphy, T. J., & Foor, C. E. (2012). "Do they even have that anymore": The impact of redesigning a minority engineering program. *Journal of Women and Minorities in Science and Engineering, 18*(3), 235–253.

Slovacek, S., Whittinghill, J., Flenoury, L., & Wiseman, D. (2012). Promoting minority success in the sciences: The minority opportunities in research programs at CSULA. *Journal of Research in Science Teaching, 49*(2), 199–217.

Strayhorn, T. L. (2008a). How college students' engagement affects personal and social learning outcomes. *Journal of College and Character, 10*(2), 1–16.

Strayhorn, T. L. (2008b). The role of supportive relationships in facilitating African American males' success in college. *NASPA Journal, 45*(1), 26–48.

Strayhorn, T. L. (2012). *College students' sense of belonging: A key to educational success for all students.* New York, NY: Routledge.

Treisman, U. (1992). Studying students studying calculus: A look at the lives of minority mathematics students in college. *College Mathematics Journal, 23*(5), 362–372.

Tsui, L. (2007). Effective strategies to increase diversity in STEM fields: A review of the research literature. *The Journal of Negro Education, 76*(4), 555–581.

Yin, R. K. (2003). *Case study research: Design and methods.* Thousand Oaks, CA: SAGE.

CHAPTER 2

THE AFFORDANCES AND CONSTRAINTS OF SOCIAL NETWORKS AMONG LATINA ENGINEERING STUDENTS

Erika Mein
Alberto Esquinca
Elsa Villa
Angelica Monarrez

This underrepresentation of women and minorities, particularly Latinas, in engineering persists in spite of more than two decades of research and interventions addressing the problem. Higher education researchers have pointed to a constellation of factors impacting the persistence and completion rates of Latino/a students, including undue financial burdens, compromised academic preparation, and social isolation (Carter, 2006; Engstrom, 2008; Kinzie, Gonyea, Shoup, & Kuh, 2008; Lord et al., 2009). Engineering education research has uncovered several trends that help explain the

Women of Color In STEM, pages 23–33
Copyright © 2021 by Information Age Publishing
All rights of reproduction in any form reserved.

continued underrepresentation of women in undergraduate engineering programs, including the absence of female role models (Henes, Bland, Darby, & McDonald, 1995), a decreased sense of belonging in male-dominated engineering programs (Tonso, 2007), and women's marginalization in teamwork as a result of gendered communication patterns (Tonso, 2006; Wolfe & Powell, 2009).

One mitigating factor that has been found to positively impact the academic experiences and retention of underrepresented students, particularly women, in STEM fields is social support (Seymour & Hewitt, 1997). While social support, especially in the form of social networks, has been explored among underrepresented students in different majors, it has received less attention within STEM fields, particularly engineering, where women and minority students have lower retention and completion rates as compared to other fields (NSF, 2017). Moreover, while research and theory from the learning sciences have shown the ways in which learning is situated, contextual, and tied to identity development (Lave & Wenger, 1991; Gee, 1996), less is known about the ways in which social networks influence the identity development of students, especially Latinas, as engineers.

This chapter draws on case study methods to explore the affordances and constraints of Latinas engineering students' social networks in their academic and professional pathways in their development as engineers. Our findings show the critical role of teacher-mentors in influencing students' academic and career paths; the paradoxical influences of familial networks; and the access to important apprenticeship experiences afforded by social networks.

THEORETICAL FRAMEWORK

This study relies on sociocultural theories of learning and identity development. As scholars conceptualize learning as a situated activity, researchers have shown how such participation is also a process of identity construction. From a sociocultural perspective, identity construction involves being recognized as a particular kind of person (Gee, 1996), in this case, as an engineer or engineering student. Gaining that recognition is a socially constructed process. Individuals may use language or other signs to signal to others their group affiliation (Brown, 2004), ranging from the use of in-group words, jargon, or references to dense grammatical constructions, such as heavily nominalized words. For example, learners' use of engineering discourse can be considered instances of identity construction, as they position themselves in a bid to become recognized as a particular kind of person. This discourse may be deployed in interactions with others within the range of social fields the learner participates in, including friendships, families, professional, or university groups (Stevens, O'Connor, Garrison, Jocund, & Amos, 2008).

For some students, potential conflict might arise as acts of identity as engineers or engineering students might clash with values in learners' other relationship networks. For instance, researchers have argued that "the most potent aspect of minority children's classroom behavior lies in the conflicting features of their communicative situation with those valued by the teacher and institution" (Brown, 2004, p. 813). Some students might reject the discourses associated and opt instead to become identified as a person who rejects institutional discourses, and language again plays a role in signaling those affiliations. Learners must see an inherent value in adopting the discourse of engineering if they are to develop engineering identities (Gee, 2005).

One site for exploring students' identity construction as engineers is their social networks. Originating in sociology, the concept of social capital has been understood as the accumulation, distribution, and exchange of resources in and through social networks (Bourdieu, 1985; Coleman, 1988), while social network theory emphasizes the social ties that exist among actors (Scott, 2000). From a social network perspective, "the social environment can be expressed as patterns or regularities in relationships among interacting units" (Wasserman & Faust, 1994, p. 3). From a social network perspective, "the social environment can be expressed as patterns or regularities in relationships among interacting units" (Wasserman & Faust, 1994, p. 3). Three key concepts within social network analysis are actor, social tie, and subgroup. According to Wasserman and Faust (1994), *actors* refer to "discrete individual, corporate, or collective social units" (p. 17). *Social ties* are the linkages between actors; examples include ties based on evaluation (e.g., friendship), biology, association or affiliation, or the transfer of material resources (Wasserman & Faust, 1994). *Subgroups* refer to "any subset of actors, and all ties among them" (Wasserman & Faust, 1994, p. 19).

Another important concept for this study comes from the work of Yosso (2005), who argues for an assets-based view of communities of color and highlights different forms of capital—including aspirational, social, linguistic, and familial—that can serve as a source of empowerment rather than marginalization for students of color. This study builds on the sociological work in social networks, as well as Yosso's concept of "community cultural wealth," to examine the influence of social ties on two Latinas' development as engineers.

RESEARCH CONTEXT: METHODS AND DATA SOURCES

This study was based at a large, Hispanic-Serving Institution (HIS) in the Paso del Norte border region of Texas, which has one of the lowest median incomes in the state. The findings were part of a larger, mixed-methods study of an undergraduate leadership engineering project funded by the U.S. Department of Education (2011–2014). One component of the project was aimed at understanding the experiences of Latina engineering students in persisting and completing their engineering studies. As part of this investigation, the research team—which was made up of two education faculty members and two doctoral students—focused on social support and social networks among participants. To explore the role of social networks in Latinas' engineering trajectories, we drew on interpretivist case study methods, which help to uncover and illuminate "the messy complexity of human experience" (Haas Dyson & Genishi, 2005, p. 3), in this case, related to three women's engineering trajectories. The three cases were purposefully selected because they were typical of what we found across many of the 51 total participants, especially among women.

The primary data sources for this study were two in-depth interviews with each participant, combined with more than 50 hours of observation of their participation in engineering workshops over 3 years and the collection of relevant artifacts. The interviews were transcribed and coded in NVivo10 for patterns and themes. An open and focused approach to coding (Emerson, Fretz, & Shaw, 2011) was used in order to gain a broad picture of Latina engineering students' social networks. Coding took place individually among all four members of the research team, and we compared codes in regular data analysis sessions through the duration of the project. For the purposes of this chapter, we focused on codes related to personal, professional, and familiar relationships, which we cross-checked with observational data. We drew on participants' interview data, as well as their survey responses and observation field notes, to construct each of the three cases presented here.

SOCIAL NETWORKS AMONG LATINA
ENGINEERING STUDENTS

Case 1: Karina

At the time of this study, Karina was enrolled as a junior and then as a graduating senior in materials and metallurgical engineering. A first-generation college student from a family of first-generation Mexican immigrants, Karina had graduated from an early college high school associated with a local community college, where she earned her associate's degree. She described her pathway to engineering first influenced by a high school math teacher, Mr. Torres, recounting:

> Initially I wasn't sure what I wanted to do and what I wanted once I graduated... and he [Mr. Torres] kind of pinpointed me out and said, "You know,

you're really good at math. I think you should consider some field in either science or some type of engineering." And so I hadn't considered, I guess, before that what I was really going to do until he asked me.

Mr. Torres not only "demanded a lot" from Karina academically, but also encouraged her to become involved in student organizations. Through one of those organizations, which she described as a professional organization for minorities in engineering, Karina had the opportunity to travel to a conference in Washington, DC, which she recalled as her "first major trip" and as "impactful," as she realized that if she stayed in school she would be able to "go places with [her] life."

Karina graduated valedictorian of her high school class and decided to enroll in the local university in large part because of the financial aid package that was offered. She chose Metallurgical and Materials Engineering (MME) as her major after talking with the MME faculty advisor, Dr. Simms, and sensing that it was a small department with frequent interactions between professors and students.

During her 2 years studying MME, Karina felt both supported and discouraged by her parents, who divorced when she was very young. She said she felt fully supported by her mom, who loved school but had to drop out early. She said that her father was "extremely supportive" but that "he doesn't really understand what it means to be pursuing a higher education." Later she said that she experienced tensions at her father's house, where she lived during high school, because her father was "very traditional, old school," and "it was really hard for me to get out of the house, even for school or work," while her brothers "always had a lot more freedom."

This experience turned out to be very difficult for Karina, to the point where she sought counseling services. In spite of the family tensions, Karina pursued her goal of completing her degree, while also taking additional internship opportunities. During the summer between her junior and senior years, she participated in a 10-week research experience at an esteemed university in California. One of the most important outcomes of this experience was connecting with students from around the country and learning about possibilities for graduate school. Karina graduated in Fall 2013, with the intent to apply to graduate school at the same university where she did research the previous summer.

Case 2: Monica

Monica began participating in this study as an entering freshman at the university. She was a *transfronteriza* (border-crossing) student who initially lived in Mexico and crossed the border daily to attend the university; all of her K–12 schooling took place in Mexico. Her father was a physics teacher, while her mother administered a small family business. From the time she was a small child, she remembered being both encouraged and pressured by her parents to succeed academically. She described her father teaching fractions at the dinner table by slicing an apple and her mother teaching her with flashcards, all before she entered kindergarten.

In terms of her academic pathway, she chose engineering based on "lots of talks with my dad," who was a physicist and who encouraged her to pursue a related, but more applied, field. She received a scholarship to attend the border university, which she said her family would not have been able to afford otherwise. She initially chose mechanical engineering as her major, but switched to MME after meeting the faculty advisor, Dr. Simms, as part of her work at the university career center. She said meeting him "was the first time [she] felt like [she] had someone, faculty-wise, supporting" her.

While studying MME, Monica also had a series of extracurricular experiences that impacted her trajectory. Among them, she participated in a 9-week summer research program for underrepresented students in STEM at a prestigious East Coast university. Through that experience she learned that she "can totally do grad school . . . because it was pretty much a mini-version of getting your PhD." She worked with a female PhD student who took Monica under her wing and who ultimately served as a role model in that Monica decided that she "really, really [does] not want to be like her when I'm in grad school because she kills herself" working. Upon graduation, Monica's intent was to apply to doctoral programs in biomedical engineering.

Case 3: Adela

Adela began participating in the study as a sophomore. She was enrolled as a civil engineering major. Both her parents graduated from college, her mother with a degree in accounting and her father with a degree in industrial engineering. Her older brothers also graduated with engineering degrees, one in electrical and the other in mechanical. Adela's family moved from Mexico to the United States when she was in the fifth grade. She remembers struggling with understanding assignments due to her language proficiency, and it was not until eight grade when she started increasing her grades.

Adela recalls that her mom gave her the choice of being a doctor, a lawyer, or a politician but her father let her choose since he did not have choice over his own degree. She views her family members as role models. She mentioned how she has always looked up to her brother, who in her view has accomplished many things as an engineer: "He's been living like the engineering life cause like he's able to buy all these cars and stuff like that you know so like I really look up to him cause they it looks like he really accomplish a lot."

Upon improving her academic performance as an eighth grader, Adela was placed into a gifted and talented (GT) program. It was in that program where she heard the word "engineering" for the first time. She talked about Mr. Arribas, her ninth grade algebra and AP calculus instructor, and how he led her into her path to engineering. She described this teacher as "kind of like my father at school," because he would show concern about her school projects. Mr. Arribas was the one who brought her, along with other students, to the university to visit the engineering department. She said that he also explained to her the different types of engineering and helped her with her decision to become an engineer.

As a civil engineering major, Adela wanted to get experience in her major so she joined the Society for Civil Engineers. As part of this organization, she joined the Concrete Canoe Committee and the Steel Bridge Team. Adela talked very enthusiastically about her learning experience in the steel bridge activities:

> I learn about engineering, you know like the hands-on experience. I can relate some of my course work and my lectures into the steel bridge, like they showed us this past week how to calculate deflection and all of that so I was able to relate what we've been learning in my mechanics class into that and I liked it.

She went into further detail in explaining the process of building the bridge, saying:

> It can be different shapes like a circle or like an eye beam, whatever, so each of those you have to calculate the deflection or like the moment of inertia and all of that so since there's different shapes you have to use different formulas . . . and then calculate the centroid, the mass and everything. So . . . [with] my team, I guess the goal was to have the lowest deflection, the lightest bridge and I guess the [least] expensive.

Adela first comments on how her participation in the steel bridge team represents a "hands-on" application of her engineering studies. In her second comment, she provides more details, explaining the use of formulas to calculate deflection in order to construct a bridge that has optimal weight, deflection, and cost. In this comment, Adela more clearly positions herself as an engineer-in-the-making through her use of terms such as *deflection*, *inertia*, and *centroid*, and in her explanation of the use of formulas to construct the bridge.

FINDINGS AND DISCUSSION

In analyzing the narratives of these three Latina engineering students, three key findings emerged: the pivotal role of teacher-mentors; the paradox of family support; and the access to apprenticeship experiences afforded by social networks.

All three Latina students attributed their decision to pursue engineering to key teacher-mentor figures in their lives. In the case of Karina, she identified her high school math teacher, Mr. Torres, as the reason for choosing engineering; in the case of Monica, her primary role model was her father, a physics teacher; for Adela, it was her high school math teacher, Mr. Arribas. In each case, the crucial ingredient seemed to be the one-on-one relationship with the teacher/parent as mentor. For Karina, she felt "pinpointed" by her teacher as a freshman and supported throughout high school; in Monica's case, conversations with her father about career choices formed the basis of her decision to pursue engineering. In college, two of the three women—Karina and Monica—identified the same teacher-mentor, Dr. Simms, who seemed to play a deciding role in their decision to study MME as opposed to other majors.

Another finding that emerged was the paradox of family support. Family was one key source of these students' community cultural wealth (Yosso, 2005). However, the case of Karina shows the double-edged nature of family as a source of positive social capital. In her case, she felt supported by her mother but hindered by her father, who she felt did not understand the meaning of pursuing a college degree. In his "traditional" ways, he tried to prevent her from leaving the house, while her brothers were granted much more freedom. Karina's case shows the complicated nature of family "support," which is tied to individual beliefs and wider cultural practices that could serve to restrict rather than open up some Latinas' academic and career paths. The cases of Monica and Adela show just the opposite: both had family support, from an early age, to pursue college. The differences among these three cases shed light on the ways in which class and gender potentially operate as interlocking forces in social networks, impacting the kinds of support that participants receive in pursuing STEM education and careers.

Finally, this study found that for both of these women, "apprenticeship" experiences (Lave, 1996) in engineering were both an outgrowth of and catalyst for social networks. In the case of Karina, her teacher-mentor Mr. Torres encouraged her to participate in student organizations that led her to take a life-changing trip to Washington DC; moreover, the networking that she gained from the 10-week research experience at a California university influenced her decision to pursue graduate school at the same university. For Monica, the research experience at an East Coast university not only connected her with an important role model but also convinced her that she was capable of pursuing a PhD. Finally, for Adela, the experience of participating on the steel bridge team provided an opportunity for her to get "hands-on" experience in civil engineering and also to practice being an engineer, not only by contributing to building a bridge and showing her appropriation of engineering discourse. In each of these instances, the women highlighted ongoing, substantive interaction with "more expert others," which influenced their own paths as engineers.

CONCLUSION

This study explores the experiences of three successful undergraduate Latinas studying engineering. In each of these cases, social support and social networks played a critical role in their development as engineering students. This support was found in the form of teacher-mentors at the middle and high school level who encouraged their pathways into engineering, as well as mentors within their undergraduate studies who served as advisors and role models of what it looked like to be an engineer, in some cases, a female engineer. While family was an important source of support for Adela and Monica, it played a more contradictory role in Karina's case, where she felt impeded by her father while supported by her mother.

This study also shows the critical role of social networks tied to apprenticeship experiences as a source of learning and identity development for Latina engineering students. Each of the three Latina students highlighted had at least one significant professional development experience with engineering where they were exposed to hands-on practice while working with individuals with more expertise. For Karina and Monica, these apprenticeship experiences helped shape their decision to pursue graduate studies in engineering; for Adela, who was a year behind the others in her studies, the steel bridge team served as a means to practice her engineering identity and to apply what she was learning in her classes.

This study contributes to a growing body of knowledge related to the retention of Latinos/as in undergraduate engineering. By examining the ways in which three Latinas' social networks influenced their career and academic trajectories, our study draws attention to the critical sources of support that schools and universities can provide to underrepresented students, especially minoritized women, both in terms of teacher-mentors and in hands-on apprenticeship experiences. To achieve greater equity and access in STEM education, more research is needed to better understand not only the nuances of social networks but also institutional mechanisms and cultural shifts necessary to enhance social support for underrepresented students, especially women.

REFERENCES

Bourdieu, P. (1985). The forms of capital. In J. G. Richardson (Ed.), *Handbook of theory and research for the sociology of education* (pp. 241–58). New York, NY: Greenwood.

Brown, B. A. (2004). Discursive identity: Assimilation into the culture of science and its implications for minority students. *Journal of Research in Science Teaching, 41*(8), 810–834.

Carter, D. F. (2006). Key issues in the persistence of underrepresented minority students. *New Directions for Institutional Research, 2006*(130), 33–46.

Coleman, J. S. (1988). Social capital in the creation of human capital. *American Journal of Sociology, 94,* S95–S120.

Emerson, R., Fretz, R., & Shaw, L. (1995). *Writing ethnographic fieldnotes.* Chicago, IL: The University of Chicago Press.

Engstrom, C. M. (2008). Curricular learning communities and unprepared students: How faculty can provide a foundation for success. *New Directions for Teaching and Learning, 2008*(115), 5–19.

Gee, J. P. (1996). *Social linguistics and literacies: Ideology in discourses.* London, England: RoutledgeFalmer.

Gee, J. P. (2005). *An introduction to discourse analysis: Theory and method* (2nd ed.). London, England: Routledge.

Haas Dyson, A., & Genishi, C. (2005). *On the case: Approaches to language and literacy research.* New York, NY: Teachers College Press.

Henes, R., Bland, M. M., Darby, J., & McDonald, K. (1995). Improving the academic environment for women engineering students through faculty workshops. *Journal of Engineering Education, 84,*1–9.

Kinzie, J., Gonyea, R., Shoup, R., & Kuh, G. D. (2008). Promoting persistence and success of underrepresented students: Lessons for teaching and learning. *New Directions for Teaching and Learning, 115,* 21–38.

Lave, J., & Wenger, E. (1991). *Situated learning: Legitimate peripheral participation.* Cambridge, England: Cambridge University Press.

Lave, J. (1996). Teaching, as learning, in practice. *Mind, Culture, and Activity, 3*(3), 149–164.

Lord, S. M., Camacho, M. M., Layton, R. A., Long, R. A., Ohland, M. W., & Washburn, M. H. (2009). Who's persisting in engineering? A comparative analysis of male and female Asian, Black, Hispanic, Native American, and White students. *Journal of Women and Minorities in Science and Engineering, 15*(2), 167–290. https://doi.org/10.1615/JWomenMinorScienEng.v15.i2.40

National Science Foundation. (2017). Women, minorities, and persons with disabilities in science and engineering. Washington, DC: Author. Retrieved from https://www.nsf.gov/statistics/2017/nsf17310/digest/about-this-report/

Scott, J. (2000/2013). *Social network analysis* (3rd ed.). London, England: SAGE.

Seymour, E., & Hewitt, N. M. (1997). *Talking about leaving: Why undergraduates leave the sciences.* Boulder, CO: Westview.

Stevens, R., O'Connor, K., Garrison, L., Jocuns, A., & Amos, D. M. (2008). Becoming an engineer: Toward a three dimensional view of learning. *Journal of Engineering Education, 97*(3), 355–368.

Tonso, K. (2006). Teams that work: Campus culture, engineer identity, and social interactions. *Journal of Engineering Education, 95*(1), 25–37.

Tonso, K. (2007). *On the outskirts of engineering: Learning identity, gender, and power via engineering practice.* Rotterdam, The Netherlands: Sense.

Wasserman, S., & Faust, K. (1994). *Social network analysis: Methods and applications.* Cambridge, England: Cambridge University Press.

Wolfe, J., & Powell, E. (2009). Biases in interpersonal communication: How engineering students perceive gender typical speech acts in teamwork. *Journal of Engineering Education, 98*(1), 5–15.

Yosso, T. (2005). Whose culture has capital? A critical race theory discussion of community cultural wealth. *Race, Ethnicity, and Education, 8*(1), 69–91.

CHAPTER 3

CHALLENGES AND SOURCES OF SUPPORT FOR LATINA UNDERGRADUATE AND GRADUATE STUDENTS IN STEM DISCIPLINES

Liza Renee Lizcano
Rosalía Chávez Zárate

The gender gap continues to persist between women and men in the fields of science, technology, engineering, and mathematics (STEM). Women continue to earn STEM degrees at a lower rate than their male counterparts (Beede et al., 2011). Women of color face additional barriers. At the undergraduate level, Latinas receive less than 5% of the bachelor's degrees awarded in STEM fields in the United States (National Science Foundation [NSF], 2013).

With an increasing Latino population (U.S. Census Bureau, 2011), these low rates of Latinas earning STEM degrees are particularly alarming. Though a number of studies have focused on factors that contribute to the

Women of Color In STEM, pages 35–53

"leaky" STEM pipeline for Latinas, it is also important to carry out research with Latinas who have successfully made it through the STEM pipeline. Using the lens of academic resilience, our research will focus on challenges that undergraduate and graduate Latina students have faced in their STEM trajectories and how they were able to overcome these obstacles.

Academic resilience is the ability to succeed in academic environments and is attributed to a number of personal traits and experiences (Gonzalez & Padilla, 1997; Wang & Gordon, 1994). Critical concepts to consider when investigating academic resilience include risk factors, or experiences that increase the probability of a negative outcome, and protective factors, which are positive experiences that shield individuals from negative circumstances (Luthar, Cicchetti, & Becker, 2000; Masten, 2001; Masten & Powell, 2003).

Flores (2011) has grouped risk factors that Latino students face when entering STEM fields into three categories: school curriculum, structural factors, and cultural factors. Structural factors can include lack of funding or documentation status and cultural factors can include gender constraints. Protective factors for Latino students in STEM majors include high SAT math scores, working on a faculty research project, and being exposed to group work in STEM classes (Crisp, Nora, & Taggart, 2009; Espinosa, 2008).

METHOD

We focus on two participants in this study who were selected from a larger study. The larger study included 15 undergraduate and 15 graduate Latina students at a selective institution. These participants were interviewed to examine their STEM trajectories at different time points while focusing on challenges, achievement, self-efficacy beliefs, and contextual factors. Prior to their interviews, participants completed an online survey to gather information about their academic background and demographic factors. Table 3.1 lists a summary of all of the participants' background information. The interviews were audio recorded with participants' consent.

The interview was divided into the following topics: early STEM experiences, high school experiences in STEM, transition to college, college experiences, and graduate school experiences (graduate students only). These interview subsections were developed to answer our guiding questions: "What are the academic trajectories for Latina students in STEM fields?"; "What are the challenges these women face in their paths?"; and "What sources of support do they draw upon to overcome these challenges?"

Using a grounded theory approach (Charmaz, 1995; Glaser & Strauss, 1967), we open-coded the audio files, interview memos, and transcripts. After the creation of the preliminary codes, we took note of the themes that emerged. Then we reread the interview materials using these themes to guide our analysis.

TABLE 3.1   Summary of Participants' Background Information From Larger Study Sample

	Number of Participants	Highest Parent Educational Attainment		K–12 School Type		Immigrant Generation	
	Engineering	HS	College Degree	Private	Public	1st	2nd or Later
Undergraduate Students	12	5	6	1	14	14	1
Science Graduate Students	7	5	2	2	5	3	4
Engineering Graduate Students	8	3	5	4	4	3	5

We first provide an overview of the major risk and protective factors that were reported among the larger study sample. Then, we focus on the academic trajectories and experiences of two of the participants: Cecilia, an undergraduate student, and Julie, a graduate student. In order to protect the participants, we have assigned them pseudonyms and changed any information that might reveal their identities. These students were selected because their experiences may be generalizable to many undergraduate and graduate students.

Cecilia was a senior in college at the time of the interview. Cecilia was born and raised in a small agricultural town in California. She has two younger sisters; at the time, one of her sisters was in 10th grade and the other was a sophomore in college. Her father arrived to the United States as a teenager and enrolled in high school for a few years. He worked mostly in agriculture but also worked as a truck driver. Her mother also had a high school education, which she earned in Mexico and was a stay at home mom. Her mother moved to the United States after she married Cecilia's father.

Julie was 29 years old at the time of the interview. She was in the third year of her doctoral program and had recently passed her qualifying exam. Julie is the oldest of four children and the first in her family to attend college and graduate school. Her parents were born in Mexico, and Julie and her siblings were born in the United States. Julie's mother completed second grade in Mexico, and Julie's father completed high school in Mexico.

MAJOR FINDINGS

The larger study sample reported struggling with diverse risk factors that impacted their self-confidence: feeling ill-prepared, unsupportive peers and professors/advisors, feeling pressured to conform to a male-dominated environment, a lack of a sense of belonging, microaggressions, and some faced racism and sexism. These women also reported experiencing a number of protective factors. Both undergraduate and graduate students reported high levels of parental support, positive educational experiences, a strengthening of their cultural identities, mentors, self-efficacy, self-motivation, resource availability, and institutional support. One of the educational programs that served as a protective factor for undergraduate students was a summer transition program for incoming students of color interested in STEM. These risk and protective factors are explored in detail through the two selected participants' interview responses.

Early STEM Experience

Cecilia's and Julie's parents had little to no formal experience with STEM education. However, both Cecilia and Julie felt that their parents encouraged their interests in STEM activities, even in early childhood. As a young girl, Cecilia enjoyed doing math. She did well in this subject and was always ahead of her peers. Her first grade teacher actually proposed that she be moved up to second grade but her parents preferred that she stay in first grade. Math initiated her interest in STEM more broadly. Cecilia's mother could only help check her math homework because her mother did not speak English very well. Cecilia remembers being by her father's side often while he fixed his truck. She mentioned how his experiences, when she first started to see engines, may have sparked her interest in mechanical engineering. She enjoyed watching her father work on the "machinery."

While Cecilia's early STEM activities involved her parents, Julie described her early STEM activities as "loner endeavors," since her parents and siblings were not involved in these activities with her. When asked about her memories of early interests in science or math, Julie replied that she often enjoyed observing animals and insects in middle school. These experiences fostered her interest in animal behavior, which she supplemented with viewings of wildlife documentaries and animal magazines. In high school, Julie pursued her interest in animal behavior by volunteering at an animal shelter.

Julie was enrolled in a variety of advanced math and science courses at her public high school and reported receiving mostly A's and B's in these classes. Julie had positive experiences in a physiology laboratory class and negative feelings about her biology classes. She reflected that her physiology teacher was engaging and created concrete, interactive learning experiences. In contrast, Julie often felt like a failure in biology class, since she did not do well and the topics were too abstract for her preferences. This was particularly frustrating for Julie since she had enjoyed the subject so much when she was younger. During the interview, Julie reflected that she may have been too hard on herself about her lower grades in biology, but she was more likely to try in her physiology class since she was good at it.

College Application and Decision Processes

The college application and decision processes were difficult experiences for both women and their parents. Cecilia's parents were concerned about her attending a college far away from home and worried about Cecilia living on her own. In her family, it was customary that women live with their families until they got married. Her parents were also concerned about men and women living in the same dormitory and visiting each other's rooms.

Though Julie's parents strongly encouraged and expected her to attend college, they were not able to help with the process. Julie reported feeling a little behind the majority of her classmates whose parents were college educated and familiar with the application process. She noticed that her friends were preparing certain aspects of the application and began preparing those sections as well. Julie reflected that her classmates were concerned with attending Ivy League schools, which was disorienting for her, since she had never heard of these schools and did not know where they were located. The only school Julie knew was the large state university about 10 minutes away from her parents' home.

Julie mentioned that, though her parents expected her to attend college, they also did not want her to attend school too far away. This feeling was amplified since Julie was the oldest daughter in the family, and Julie's parents "just weren't ready to have one of their kids move out." Because of her late start in the application process and expectations for her to stay close to home, Julie chose to attend the state university in her hometown. She lived at home and commuted to school until graduation. Though this decision was convenient and comfortable, Julie mentioned that she felt "embarrassed and stupid" that she had not planned for college to the same extent as the other students in her advanced placement classes.

A major concern for both Julie and her parents was finding money to pay for college. Julie reports that her parents had an "idealistic" view of the financial aid process, expecting her to receive enough scholarships to cover her tuition and living expenses. Since Julie was the oldest child and was fairly self-sufficient, her parents also expected her to complete financial aid applications on her own. Julie reflected that it would have been helpful for her parents to speak with other parents about helping your child with the financial aid and college application processes. However, her parents' networks consisted of Julie's aunts and uncles. Since Julie's cousins had not attended college, her aunts and uncles did not have that information.

Transition to College

Cecilia felt that many teachers at her high school did not have high expectations for their students. Cecilia was terrified as she arrived at her university and had several doubts about her ability to succeed. She was worried about not making friends and not liking the university. Her father noticed her fear and told Cecilia not to worry and that if she did not like the university, she could come back home. Though this was comforting for her, she also felt that if she did not stay she would not be disappointing them. This was not motivating for Cecilia. However, since she knew that her parents wanted her to do well and go to college, she was glad her parents did not place pressure on her like some of her classmates' parents. Her peers' parents even placed pressure on them to pursue STEM. Cecilia liked having a choice in her major selection.

Major Selection

Julie majored and minored in science fields. This decision stemmed from her earlier interest in physiology and biology. Julie's father also suggested that she pursue a science field, due to future job opportunities. While choosing her major, Julie's decision centered on the classes that made her happy. These classes were often medically related or biology classes. Julie also reported enjoying her humanities classes, such as women's studies, and briefly thought about changing her major. However, Julie decided to major in a science field due to the increased job opportunities for a graduate with a STEM degree.

When Cecilia arrived at her university, she was undecided about the major she would declare. She considered pursuing engineering, psychology, architectural engineering, or product design. Cecilia decided to start taking courses that fulfilled the engineering requirements. She reasoned that if she decided to switch to another major it would be easier to switch from engineering to another field, given that engineering had more required courses. Additionally, Cecilia's advisor, Raul, one of the deans in the engineering department, encouraged her to take a class in each engineering major she was considering. As Cecilia thought back to her first year, she mentioned how she was not ready to pick one major because she did not really know about engineering.

Cecilia took an introductory course to aeronautics and astronautics and was fascinated by it; this became her initial major. She had a prior interest in airplanes and space shuttles, and she enjoyed the content of the course. The instructor was a Hispanic professor who worked for NASA and frequently discussed his work in class. Cecilia was intrigued by his work and thought it was "very cool and interesting." However, Cecilia later decided to switch to mechanical engineering because she felt that this major allowed more flexibility when it came to future job prospects.

Cecilia also mentioned how she did not feel encouraged to continue as an aeronautics and astronautics major because the staff in that department were not the most amiable. She mentioned how Sara, the woman that was responsible for overseeing the students who declared a major in aeronautics and astronautics, kept asking Cecilia if she was sure about continuing in that major. Sara stated that there were only nine students in that major and that Cecilia's diploma would not say "Aeronautics and Astronautics," it would only say "Engineering." Hearing, "Are you sure?" had Cecilia questioning herself. Initially, Cecilia thought to herself, "Yes I'm really sure," but by the end she thought, "Oh wait, am I sure? I don't know if I want to do this." Cecilia took time to herself and decided to switch to mechanical engineering.

Undergraduate Experiences

General Challenges

Cecilia felt that her high school calculus class was the only class that prepared her for college, though she still felt that she was more behind than her peers. She did well in her first university math course with additional help from a math program for low-income diversity students. Cecilia noted that she did not know how to study for class or exams. This program helped her through the process. Cecilia did not feel comfortable participating in class because she was self-conscious about her writing and how she spoke. In STEM courses, she only asked questions after class was over. Cecilia also struggled selecting courses. Raul assisted her in this process. Initially, it was also difficult for Cecilia to approach professors. Older students would often advise her to attend office hours, but Cecilia felt intimidated. She had to gain the courage to attend office hours and work with her peers.

As Cecilia progressed through her courses there continued to be instances where she felt overwhelmed and underprepared, and continued to do worse than some peers. Other students had a stronger background that she felt prepared them better for college and these challenging courses. She had peers who mentioned they felt very prepared coming to college from high school and had done particularly well since the beginning of college. Cecilia felt that she had to catch up and that she was still behind. However, there were instances where she felt that she was at her "peers' level" or "on track." For example, when she was sharing ideas for a project and her colleagues would tell her, "Oh, that's a good idea. I hadn't thought about that."

Group Work

One of Cecilia's challenges also included having to adjust to working with a team. She did not have much exposure to students of other racial backgrounds in her past academic experience so she felt embarrassed when trying to talk to other students. If she heard that she was going to have to work with a team, it was difficult for her to simply approach someone. She did find it beneficial to have a group where they could help another. However, when thinking about who to approach she would ask herself, "What if they don't want to work with me or don't like me?" or "What if I'm not doing as well as them in class? I'm pulling them down." If she did not previously know another student in her course or felt uncomfortable asking, she would not approach anyone and would end up doing worse in the course. During the time of the interview, she described how she was in a course where she knew she had to approach someone but had been putting it off because she was afraid to do so. When working in groups, she would tend to gravitate towards other women and minorities, although she rarely formed her own study groups. Overall, she would regularly work on homework by herself or go to office hours.

Failure

Cecilia struggled with coursework, and it was difficult for her to stay motivated after experiencing failure. She recalled failing one of her midterms freshman year, which was one of the most discouraging moments of her college years. Fortunately, she mentioned, she was able to receive tutoring, started going to her teaching assistants and professor's office hours, and asked for help on everything that she could. She earned a perfect score on the second midterm and did well on her class final. After seeing how well she performed on the second midterm and final, she felt that she could do this. All she needed to do was put more effort into her courses and assignments. It was a great learning experience for Cecilia.

Professors

Cecilia had positive and negative experiences with professors. Thus far, Cecilia had not had a female professor in engineering, which was discouraging for her. She also described that there were a few times where she felt discouraged by professors or courses, but it was more of a feeling of intimidation. She felt that professors were too busy. She feared that she was not at the "level" she should be when she spoke to a professor. She would question herself on what she asked professors. She would think, "Did I say something stupid?" Cecilia mentioned that professors did not say anything "mean" in particular, but she felt a vibe.

Overall, in terms of the rest of her engineering professors, Cecilia described them as "pretty welcoming and open." Some had been intimidating, and she did not like to converse with them, and there were also a few professors who would stay until one or two in the morning helping students finish their projects. Seeing professors take the time to help their students to that extent made her feel a lot better about being in those courses.

Parental Support

Despite the fact that Cecilia's parents do not fully understand her major or coursework, they are very supportive. They remind her how proud they are of her and what she has accomplished, such as the internships she has taken part in and her experience in aerospace. They love to share this with others and say that she has helped build airplanes.

In addition to emotional support, they did their best to provide "instrumental support." Whenever Cecilia would mention that she had a lot of work to do, they would always ask if there was anything they could assist her with. For one of her manufacturing courses, she had to build her own project, this included sanding down her piece. Her parents spent the entire weekend helping her sand down her project, as they watched *novelas*.

Similar to her experience with Sara, one of the only things that her parents have done that has made her feel discouraged is questioning her intent. They questioned the out-of-state internship she wanted to accept by asking her questions like, "Are you sure about this?" However, they do not explicitly discourage her or tell her that she cannot or should not go.

Mentors

Cecilia received different assistance, guidance, and support from three mentors at her institution. Cecilia had a professor, Professor Ryan, for a series of three courses. She described how Professor Ryan did not necessarily notice her in the first quarter. She did not approach him often until she learned that she should attend office hours her second quarter and approached him there. Professor Ryan noticed that she was attending office hours and her improvement in the class. He cared about how she was doing in the course, showed interest, and would ask about her family. She felt Professor Ryan was very encouraging of Latinas in engineering as well because his wife was Latina and had also studied engineering. She felt that Professor Ryan cared at least slightly more than the average professor.

Another individual who helped Cecilia was her advisor Raul whom she would meet with often. He helped her understand joint bachelor's and master's programs that the institution offered. Also, he advised her on how she could find funding for her program and obtain a teaching assistantship. Her third mentor was her major advisor, Jay. She chose him as a mentor after she spoke to other students who mentioned that he was "pretty cool" and a very nice person. She would meet with him on occasion to discuss how her school-work was going. She considered Jay a mentor because he was always available to meet with her, which was not the case with all professors.

Cultural Identity

During her time in school, Cecilia joined diverse on-campus organizations. In terms of STEM, she became involved in an organization that developed a solar-powered vehicle, which she joined out of personal interest. She was also part of another organization that targeted Latino students in engineering (LSE), which people in her dormitory encouraged her to join. She also thought LSE would be a good place to make friends who shared similar interests and a place to obtain mentoring from older students. In class she learned concepts, but this organization helped her prepare for a career in engineering. LSE hosted resume workshops, gave her the opportunity to work on an "elevator pitch," and helped her attend conferences such as the Society of Hispanic Professional Engineers (SHPE). Cecilia also joined study groups with her classmates in LSE.

Research Opportunities

During her undergraduate studies, Julie obtained a part-time job at a nearby private university working on clinical research projects. She also joined a pre-medical organization at the private university. Julie was a member of the organization during all four years and worked with other students to provide medical interpreter services for a local hospital for patients who only spoke Spanish. Julie reported that she was glad she found the group because it was "really, really meaningful work that [she] enjoyed." During the last two years of her undergraduate education, Julie participated in two clinical research and community education internships in Honduras. These experiences all provided Julie with practical skills and research experience. In addition, they heightened Julie's interest in people's well-being. Julie felt a strong desire to use research as a way to provide answers for these patients' problems.

Julie also had the opportunity to join a research group at her undergraduate university. She reflected that the principal investigator for the group was a member of an underrepresented group. This professor served as a research mentor for Julie and was very encouraging of women and other underrepresented students in the lab in general. Through this experience, Julie was able to learn how to execute a research project and presented posters of her findings. She was also able to connect with other biology-related interest groups.

Cecilia had several positive experiences taking part in research and internships. She participated in a research program for minority students in Colorado the summer after her sophomore year and in an internship in Arizona. Both of these programs were in aerospace. She found out about both of these opportunities through her advisor, Raul. He also introduced her to past alumni who helped her prepare for the internship position.

Prior to attending the research program Cecilia considered switching from mechanical engineering to computer science. She planned to make this decision during her research program. Indeed, the research program did help in this decision. She realized that she enjoyed building and testing models more than coding and chose to stay in mechanical engineering. Additionally, the internship gave her the opportunity to experience working in an office space in a large company. She recognized that she did not enjoy working with a large company because it took a very long time to have projects and work approved.

These experiences helped her decide what her focus would be in her master's program, and helped give her confidence through the positive reinforcement that she received. Her manager as well as other mentors at the company expressed that they wanted her to come back and liked the work that she did. Halfway through her internship opportunity she was offered a full-time job for the following year. Being at a competitive institution there were times when Cecilia was building a project and thought to herself, "How do they expect me to do this?" or looked at a problem set and did not know where to start. At times, she felt that she was "barely getting by" and felt "mediocre." Taking part in internships and research projects gave her a chance to see how she would do in the real word. She left feeling that she was doing okay, and that she would be able to find a job after she graduated.

Cecilia began to see herself as an engineer when she took part in her internship. She described how when she worked on projects for class, she continued to feel like a student because she was still guided by the professor. If she was "stuck" on her project or coursework she would go to other people to see how they were doing. If she was stuck on a project or work in her internship, she would approach other more experienced engineers. However, she recognized that these were actual engineering problems that did not have a solution, not problems that a professor generated with a solution. Additionally, the solutions she produced during her internship were not examined to see if they were correct or incorrect. Her employers trusted her solution.

Discrimination in Undergraduate Classes

Another challenge that Cecilia experienced in her undergraduate career was dealing with a feeling of discomfort with her male peers. She mentioned how in one of her courses on vehicle dynamics there were 50 students, and she was one of four girls. Cecilia was generally quiet in courses such as these because she felt that she had to be careful about what she said so she would be taken seriously. She had to think clearly about the ideas she would say aloud.

Additionally, being part of a male-dominated field added pressure to Cecilia. She would think, "What if women aren't smart enough to do these engineering things?" She would worry about asking a "stupid question," and males thinking, "Oh this is why women are dumb and can't do engineering." This feeling would discourage her from asking questions in class. Instead, she would wait until after class to approach the professor or the teaching assistant. Cecilia felt more comfortable voicing her opinion in her "design classes" in the design school where she felt that creativity was valued more. She felt it was a place where she had a different perspective to offer, a perspective that was appreciated.

Transition to Graduate School

After college graduation, Julie worked in industry for a few years. She took this step to pay off her debts from college and to figure out the next step in her career path and decide if she wanted to attend medical school or graduate school. Julie's parents knew that working in industry was just a temporary job, but they expected her to attend medical school and were confused about the change in plans. In contrast to her undergraduate application process, Julie stated that she felt very "in control" of the graduate application process and was confident about her potential to enter graduate school. She had secured strong letters of recommendation, had recently published some of the findings from her research project during her undergraduate education, and had researched graduate schools and faculty members. Julie applied to and was accepted at a number of doctoral programs and decided to attend a private university on the East Coast. Though she had a great experience at the university, Julie decided to leave the program with her master's degree. Julie made this decision based on family circumstances and transferred to a doctoral program at a private university near her parents' home.

Graduate School Experiences

Mentors
Julie described having supportive mentors and a strong support network at both of her graduate universities. Most of her mentors have been older

graduate students in her research groups. Julie pointed out that these students were great resources, since they understood the daily requirements of research and had just recently passed through the same obstacles. Julie's advisor at her first graduate institution was also a strong influence. This advisor was a young female untenured professor. Julie was thrilled to be in the professor's lab, since she had never had a female academic mentor or a female biology professor. Julie noted that females in these positions "just don't exist."

While her male advisor at her current graduate university was also helpful, Julie noted that she felt there were not many other faculty members whom she considered to be supportive. Julie reflected that this may have been due to the much larger size of her current graduate university as compared to her first graduate university. She felt that faculty members at her current university were "less accessible" and that it was difficult to "form strong, long, meaningful connections with faculty unless you're super impressive. To compensate for this lack of faculty mentors, Julie created a support network which included mentors from industry and postdoctoral scholars in her research group.

Service

Julie was more active in social and service groups during her undergraduate years than her graduate school years. During graduate school, she tried to be more selective about her service activities, otherwise she worried that she "wouldn't get anything done." Though Julie did not believe her background affected her research interests, she did feel that it affected the service groups she joined. Julie felt a strong urge to help with programs that she believed made an impact, such as programs that encouraged females and students of color to pursue STEM fields. She was particularly interested in mentoring Latinas interested in STEM, since she felt that when "you come from a culture that's so collective, when you branch out and do something different, you feel very alone."

Finding Balance

In regards to balance, Julie noticed patterns based on how well her research was going. When experiments went well she would put all of her energy into her projects and spend less time with family. During these research-focused periods, Julie's parents often asked her when she would be able to visit. This was fairly stressful for Julie, since she felt that she should stay at school and focus on her work while also trying to fulfill family expectations and obligations. On the other hand, when she had trouble with an experiment, Julie would try to spend more time with friends and family in an effort "to forget about all of the failures."

Failure

When Julie experienced failures, she reported that she sometimes attributed this failure to her gender, but almost never attributed failure to her racial/ethnic background. Failure was also related to feelings of loneliness, since Julie's experiments were often completed independently. The frustration of the failures caused Julie to ask herself, "How many more times do I have to do this to make it work?" and "When am I going to graduate?" Though she tried not to dwell on the failures, she also noted "You just want to feel like there is forward movement and that you're one step closer to graduating." Though Julie sometimes worried about being judged by others for her mistakes or failures, she tried to ignore these feelings. Julie stated, "In grad school, you sort of have to create thick skin for yourself and not care about what people think." However she also added, "It's hard for someone who is sort of sensitive to develop that thick skin to survive."

Questioning Decision to Enter Graduate School

Though Julie reported feeling a sense of belonging at her current university and in her department, she also wondered "if graduate school was worth it" and asked herself why she was sacrificing years of her life to get a doctoral degree. These thoughts were especially prominent as her friends and family were getting married, starting families, and working at their dream jobs. Julie summarized by stating that, in graduate school, "everything's on pause, but you also see everyone else progress, so you just feel like you're falling behind." Julie viewed graduate school as a path toward her future career, but she wondered "if [she] could do it all over" if there were alternate paths toward her dream job that she could have followed.

Qualifying Exam

In addition to all of the emotional stress that graduate school elicits, Julie was concerned about preparing for and passing her qualifying exam. Julie mentioned that she had little to no guidance from her advisor about her project. This was particularly frustrating for Julie since she had just passed her qualifying exam at the institution where she received her master's degree. Julie was able to receive some help from a postdoctoral scholar in her group, and she also spoke to other students about the process. After "lots of pep talks," she was able to complete her projects and reported doing well. Julie summarized her approach to all of these challenges by saying that "grad school is understanding that there are problems, but they have solutions, and you need to put yourself in the right mindset to pull through."

Discrimination in the Workplace and Graduate School

Julie noted that most discrimination she has experienced has been very subtle. This made it hard for Julie to determine if the experience was actually discriminatory or not. During her time in industry, Julie felt there was a lack of respect in the environment. She reflected that the lack of respect may have potentially been due to her age and gender. At the company, Julie was the youngest employee but also one of the few employees with a science degree. She also reported experiencing sexual harassment in the workplace. Julie stated that these experiences made her a stronger individual. This experience also led Julie to act on her desire to return to graduate school, though she knew it would lead to a significant pay cut. Julie wanted to earn a doctoral degree in order to return to places like this company and "contribute something meaningful without ever having to explain [herself] or [her] credibility in science."

In graduate school, Julie stated that there was no blatant discrimination, but she mentioned that some experiences made her feel uncomfortable. Though her advisor was supportive, she also felt that he went out of his way to mention how great it was to work with a group of strong female researchers. While Julie appreciated his effort to be inclusive, she also felt that those types of comments should be unnecessary. Julie also noticed that there were different expectations for lab members depending on their gender. She felt there was an underlying feeling that women would not attempt riskier projects because they would not pursue academia. When Julie told her advisor that she would like to pursue industry after graduation, she felt that he made the assumption that it was because she wanted more flexibility with her family. Though he was supportive of the decision, Julie felt judged for her intentions without having discussed her reasoning behind the decision. Julie also noted that there was a discrepancy in the expectations about how male and female graduate students spent their time. She mentioned that it was expected that women were more likely to participate in service organizations, while men were expected to spend most of their time on research activities.

Gender Imbalance and Concerns About Future Career

When asked about the gender distribution in her program, Julie responded that there were about equal numbers of male and female graduate students. She added that there was "a huge dropoff between compositions of males and females for grad school versus postdocs versus beyond." Julie further explained that professors and leaders in the program were often males and that "women just fall off." Julie remarked that though many people believe women do not pursue academic and leadership positions due to "the baby component," she did not believe that women should have to choose to have an academic job or have a child. Rather, Julie believed that the culture of the field needed to change, since it had been male-dominated for so long. Julie pointed out that women with children needed resources that had never been considered in the male-dominated workplace. If the field hopes to attract women, Julie believed that the culture needed to change to accommodate women with children. Though Julie felt that she would be able to find a good job after graduating from her doctoral program, she also worried that she might not be able to balance a high-powered leadership job with having a family and demonstrating competence, since the support structures may not be in place by the time she will be ready to enter the job market.

DISCUSSION

This research contributes to the few studies on Latina women in STEM at the undergraduate and graduate levels. It is one of the only studies that investigate Latinas at a private, competitive institution. These results offer knowledge of the barriers and sources of support that Latina women encounter in their pathway into STEM.

Our findings point not just to the need for mentors, but also point to different ways that mentors can support Latinas and other students. This private institution had a number of resources available to students, such as summer programs, research opportunities, and administrators who specialized in working with underrepresented students. One administrator was identified as a mentor in more than half of the 30 interviews that we conducted. This administrator and other mentors provided students with concrete advice on how to connect with professors, emphasized the importance of research experiences, connected them with potential internships or jobs, and provided emotional support. Without these mentors, our participants might not have known how to prepare themselves for graduate school or their future careers.

Though both women's parents were very supportive of their decisions about STEM and college, both women also reported that they would have liked their parents to have provided more guidance during the college application and decision processes. As Julie suggested, it would have been helpful if her parents could have received this information from their friend and family networks. Cecilia also appreciated her parents' support but would have liked them to help motivate her by having higher expectations rather than telling her she could return home if she did not like her university.

Espinosa (2008) found that being able to work on a faculty's research project was a strong predictor of academic self-concept for Latino students. We found that research opportunities were also essential for our female participants and inspired them to obtain advanced degrees. The participants reported that their first experiences with STEM activities occurred early in their education, but they did not have a clear idea about scientists' and engineers' responsibilities until they participated in research. Research experiences were also helpful in providing the participants with opportunities to recognize what types of projects they did and did not enjoy. Espinosa also found that Latinas academic self-concept was positively impacted by being exposed to group work in STEM courses. However, in our interviews, participants often mentioned that though they saw the benefit of group work, many preferred to work alone. This decision may be due to the influence of "stereotype threat" as Lord and Camacho (2013) mention or the competitive environment within groups as found by Camacho and Lord (2011).

Both women experienced microaggressions (Sue et al., 2007) or "brief, everyday exchanges that send denigrating messages" (p. 273) to people in minority groups. The participants had to deal with these experiences on their own and sometimes chose to address the comments directly. It would be helpful for the participants if their mentors or advisors were able to help facilitate these discussions. However, sometimes the advisors or mentors were the people committing the microaggressions, so students might need additional sources of support to help with these experiences. Though women experienced microaggressions relating to their gender and ethnicity, they received more comments based on their gender. Similarly, Lord and Camacho (2013) also found that Latinas in engineering were more influenced by gender stereotypes rather than those related to ethnicity.

Contrary to previous findings (e.g., Camacho & Lord, 2011), the Latinas we interviewed expressed happiness at their institution. The resource availability and particularly their resilience have helped them remain persistent despite the challenges. Nonetheless, we have to keep in mind the limitations of our study. One limitation is the generalizability of the findings, since the sample population may be viewed as an elite group of high achieving women whose experiences may not resonate with other students.

These findings give researchers and educators an opportunity to continue to learn how women navigate the double bind of being Latina and a woman in STEM disciplines. These findings may be useful in thinking of ways to implement effective intervention programs that can assist in increasing enrollment and retention of Latina women, as well as other women of color in STEM. Additionally, this helps us think about how information related to STEM majors and careers is presented to women, how to address the need for their unique perspectives, and how we can serve advisors and universities in thinking of methods to assist students in their transition to STEM/college and ways to help them succeed in STEM fields.

REFERENCES

Beede, D., Julian, T., Langdon, D., McKittrick, G., Khan, B., & Doms, M. (2011). *Women in STEM: A gender gap to innovation* (ESA Issue Brief# 04-11). Washington, DC: US Department of Commerce.

Camacho, M. M., & Lord, S. M. (2011, October). "Microaggressions" in engineering education: Climate for Asian, Latina, and White women. In *Proceedings: 41st Frontiers in Education Conference* (pp. S3H-1–S3H-6). Piscataway, NJ: IEEE.

Charmaz, K. (1995). Grounded theory. In J. A. Smith, R. Harré, & L. vanLangenhove (Eds.), *Rethinking methods in psychology* (pp. 83–122). London, England: SAGE.

Crisp, G., Nora, A., & Taggart, A. (2009). Student characteristics, pre-college, college, and environmental factors as predictors of majoring in and earning a STEM degree: An analysis of students attending a Hispanic Serving Institution. *American Educational Research Journal, 46*(4), 924–942. https://doi.org/10.3102/0002831209349460

Espinosa, L. L. (2008). The academic self-concept of African American and Latina (o) men and women in STEM majors. *Journal of Women and Minorities in Science and Engineering, 14*(2), 177–200.

Flores, G. M. (2011). Latino/as in the hard sciences: Increasing Latina/o participation in science, technology, engineering and math (STEM) related fields. *Latino Studies, 9*(2/3), 327–335. https://doi.org/10.1057/lst.2011.36

Glaser, B., & Strauss, A. (1967). *The discovery of grounded theory: Strategies for qualitative research.* London, England: Weidenfield & Nicolson.

Gonzalez, R., & Padilla, A. M. (1997). The academic resilience of Mexican American high school students. *Hispanic Journal of Behavioral Sciences, 19*(3), 301–317. https://doi.org/10.1177/07399863970193004

Lord, S. M., & Camacho, M. M. (2013, October). Latinos and Latinas in the borderlands of education: Researching minority populations in engineering. In *Proceedings: Frontiers in Education Conference* (pp. 561–566). Piscataway, NJ: IEEE.

Luthar, S. S., Cicchetti, D., & Becker, B. (2000). The construct of resilience: A critical evaluation and guidelines for future work. *Child Development, 71*(3), 543–562.

Masten, A. S. (2001). Ordinary magic: Resilience processes in development. *American Psychologist, 56*(3), 227–238.

Masten, A. S., & Powell, J. L. (2003). A resilience framework for research, policy and practice. In S. S. Luthar (Ed.), *Resilience and vulnerability: Adaptation in the context of childhood adversities* (pp. 1–25). Cambridge, England: Cambridge University Press.

National Science Foundation, & National Center for Science and Engineering Statistics. (2013). *Women, minorities, and persons with disabilities in science and engineering: 2013* (Special Report NSF 13-304). Arlington, VA. Retrieved from http://www.nsf.gov/statistics/wmpd/

Sue, D. W., Capodilupo, C. M., Torino, G. C., Bucceri, J. M., Holder, A., Nadal, K. L., & Esquilin, M. (2007). Racial microaggressions in everyday life: Implications for clinical practice. *American psychologist, 62*(4), 271.

U.S. Census Bureau. (2011). *The Hispanic population: 2010.* Retrieved from http://www.census.gov/prod/cen2010/briefs/c2010br-04.pdf

Wang, M. C., & Gordon, E. W. (1994). *Educational resilience in inner-city America: Challenges and prospects.* Philadelphia, PA: Psychology Press.

CHAPTER 4

CLOSING FACULTY RANKS

Black Women Mathematics Education Faculty Navigating Across Career Stages

Erika Bullock
Jacqueline Leonard
Joi Spencer
Erica Walker

The dearth of research concerning girls and women of color in STEM has been a consistent challenge for those interested in improving participation rates and conditions. This volume was born in response to this challenge. A significant portion of this scant documentation focuses on girls and women of color's participation as students and as scientists and engineers. According to this literature, the STEM pipeline seems to flow toward careers in the natural, physical, and technical sciences, engineering, and mathematics. However, the reality is that the STEM pipeline is less a pathway and more of a system consisting of STEM professionals in corporate, community, and educational spaces that support girls and women of color in accessing STEM-related brilliance and moving into various parts of the system to support later generations in their passage.

Women of Color In STEM, pages 55–70

Perhaps one of the least glamorous—and surely the least lucrative—STEM career option is K–12 teaching. Less prominent, however, is teacher education, a field whose critical role in developing strong STEM teachers to hone STEM competencies in girls and young women of color cannot be overlooked, particularly because "inadequate academic preparation in elementary and secondary schools" is one of the primary hindrances to success in STEM (Perna et al., 2009, p. 3). However, the teacher educator's role is not limited to teacher preparation. She also has a hand in teacher professional development, assessment writing and evaluation, curriculum and policy development, and research that builds the knowledge base related to girls and women of color in STEM. Thus, it is important to recognize teacher educators as critical contributors to the larger STEM system and to examine female teacher educators of color's experiences and methodologies for constructing educational experiences that support increased STEM participation for girls and women of color. In this chapter, we bring light to the teacher educator's role in the STEM system. Here, four Black female professors of mathematics education at different ranks (i.e., assistant professor, associate professor, and full professor) and different universities present counterstories of their experiences as co-constructors of knowledge as they examine ways to engage in *deliberate discourse* about race, ethnicity, gender, and class in mathematics education. Each author reflects on her experiences as a mathematics student, teacher, and teacher educator in a predominately White institution. The cross-case analyses of these counterstories reveal opportunities and challenges for Black women whose work focuses on bringing children of color from the margins and into full participation in mathematics.

We are "everyday academic women" (Phillips & McCaskill, 1995, p. 1012) who individually align ourselves with an agenda of social justice and culturally relevant pedagogy that permeates our scholarship, teaching, and service. Such commitments are born of personal experience and a sense of responsibility to use educational and social privilege to respond to historic and present injustices perpetuated against the Black community (Phillips & McCaskill, 1995). Black women traditionally assume the role of community caretakers. As such, Black women faculty in predominately White institutions must reconcile the deeply personal nature of these commitments with the culture and demands of the academy and use the strategies that they employ in home and community to address the double bind of racism and sexism in the university (Phillips & McCaskill, 1995). Often, the harsh realities of the challenges Black women face in academe are presented through narratives of struggle and oppression. In this chapter, the authors acknowledge the oppression of Black women in academic spaces and respond with narratives that demonstrate how "[their] Black womanness...has become [their] secret weapon for both the liberation of more sisters and the revolutionizing of the academy itself" (Phillips & McCaskill, 1995, pp. 1009–1010).

Thus, the counter-stories of Black female professors in teacher education provide a social context that reveals how our experiences are "affected by history, social structure and culture" (Holt, 2003, p. 2). These counter-stories add to the literature on critical race theory (Delgado, 2012) and Black feminist thought (Collins, 2009), particularly as it relates to our identity, agency, and resilience in the academy. Counter-stories allow us as Black women who have been successful mathematics teachers and teacher educators to revise the dominant history of Black women in mathematics education (White, 2001). They also speak to broader racial and social justice issues: (a) rhetoric versus action and behavior; (b) racial *micro-aggressions* toward faculty and students of color; and (c) *positionality* in terms of race, gender, culture, and class. Black female faculty perceptions of their teaching, research, service, and job satisfaction in settings where teacher candidates are predominantly White and female add to the extant literature on teacher education within mathematics education.

THEORETICAL FRAMEWORK

Black feminist thought (Collins, 2009) and endarkened feminist epistemology (Dillard, 2000; Dillard & Okpalaoka, 2011) provide the theoretical framework for this analysis. The principles of these epistemologies rely on two types of knowing that derive from Black women's experience—knowledge and wisdom (Collins, 2009)—and on the notion of "research as responsibility" (Dillard, 2000, p. 663) rooted in *Ubuntu*, an African collectivist paradigm that states, "I am because we are" (Dillard & Okpalaoka, 2011). In this way, Black women from all walks of life (e.g., domestics to women in academia, politics, and business) participate in a type of knowledge that is based on collective experiences that emerge from similar forms of oppression. Black feminist thought uses dialogue to assess knowledge claims, promoting an ethic of care that is characterized by "personal expressiveness, emotions, and empathy...central to the knowledge validation process" and the ethic of personal accountability (Collins, 2009, p. 281–282). Thus, Black women validate each other's experiences through dialogue and storytelling, which has roots in "African-based oral traditions and in African-American culture" (Collins, 2009, p. 279).

Using Black feminist thought allows analysts to represent Black women's experiences as individual manifestations of collective challenges. Collins (2000) warned, "Despite the common challenges confronting African-American women as a group, individual Black women neither have identical experiences nor interpret experiences in a similar fashion" (p. 30).

We use counter-narratives to highlight experiential diversity as it relates to these common challenges and to resist any effort to represent these challenges as evidence of a monolithic Black woman experience in academe.

The analysis of Black women's work is a central element of Black feminism (Collins, 2000). Collins (2000) identified two key themes related to the Black feminist analysis of Black women's paid and unpaid work. First, in studying Black women's location within labor markets, "African-American women are often presented as constrained but empowered figures, even in extremely difficult labor market settings" (p. 52). Analyses of Black women's work capture the resiliency of mind, body, and spirit required to persist in labor while facing structural racism and sexism that seek to render us inadequate, insufficient, and less-than-human (Dillard & Okpalaoka, 2011). The second theme relates to the unpaid, extended, and immediate family and community labor of Black women, which, according to Collins (2000), is a mode of resistance to oppression rather than subjugation by men. This unpaid labor often manifests as a form of community caretaking in which Black women assume responsibility for the wellbeing—broadly defined—of the community, as defined by familial relation, geography, race, class, and/or gender. Thus, Black women are motivated by a sense of sacred responsibility to something larger than ourselves (Dillard & Okpalaoka, 2011). In this study of the experiences of Black women mathematics education faculty, we engage both of these themes as we examine Black women's positions as academic and intellectual laborers and as caretakers of the community of Black girls and women in mathematics.

METHODS

We position this study within an ethnographic research paradigm, adapting counter-storytelling and phenomenology as analytical approaches to highlight Black female faculty experiences in White institutional space. In this chapter, we employ Solórzano and Yasso's (2002) counter-storytelling strategy of telling personal narratives in first-person. Using data from the experiences of four Black female professors across ranks, institutions, and regions of the United States, we examine themes across these experiences.

To investigate the treatment of Black female faculty in mathematics education through counter-narrative, we use a phenomenological approach. Phenomenological research seeks to study and enlighten lived experiences built on the following characteristics:

- Describe experiences... through, avoiding as much as possible causal explanations, generalizations, or abstract interpretations.

- Describe experiences from inside, as it were almost like a state of mind including the feelings, the mood, the emotions.
- Focus on a particular example or incident as the object of the experience; describe specific events, an adventure, a happening, a particular experience.
- Focus on an example of the experiences which stands out for its vividness, or as it was the first time.
- Attend to how the body feels, how things smell, how they sound.
- Avoid trying to beautify the account with fancy phases or flowery terminology (Van Manen, 1990, pp. 66–67).

Author 1's Counterstory

On the day that the mathematics department chair in the high school where I first taught tapped me to teach AP Calculus, I went home and penned a letter to my 10th grade mathematics teacher. This note of thanks was not one that may have been read for her retirement party as evidence of the hundreds of lives she touched. Rather, I thanked her—a White woman—for registering concern about my hard-earned Bs and Cs, for encouraging me to move out of her honors course into a lower-level class "with the other Black kids," and for all but ignoring me when I refused. When I consider what compelled me to pursue an undergraduate degree in computer science and to become a mathematics teacher and teacher educator, my mind travels first to that 10th grade class; then to the science and mathematics faculty of Spelman College, the historically Black college for women where I was encouraged to recognize my brilliance; and, finally, to the legacy of education and advocacy established by my maternal grandparents. As a high school teacher, I vowed that I would *never* allow a student to sit in my classroom feeling hurt, betrayed, ostracized, and incompetent like I did day after day. Although I was not a great mathematics student, I was quite mathematical and always worked hard to navigate courses successfully despite not feeling accepted or acceptable. I contend that my struggles with mathematics helped me to be a good mathematics teacher and to fight for those who also feel excluded. As a mathematics teacher educator, I have a new opportunity to create access pathways to mathematics for Black children by calling their current and potential teachers to recognize and encourage their brilliance.

After one year as a professor, I know that I am exactly where I am supposed to be. This position grants me the platform to affect mathematics education through curriculum, policy, and pedagogy, but my experiential location requires that I dedicate myself to using the platform to advocate on behalf of other Black girls who feel isolated in their mathematics classes.

However, it is not easy to maintain a focus on advocacy and activism while negotiating the pre-tenure faculty landscape. How do I focus on preparing teachers not to create environments of distrust and exclusion in their classrooms when they often resemble, in appearance and in word, the teacher who wounded me? How do I situate advocacy and activism as pillars of my research agenda when my questions and my work can be perceived as controversial? How do I persist through rejection and avoid the trap of Black woman's work (Collins, 2009) in my department and university?

As I wrestle with these questions, I have no answers, but I find solace in the community of Black women scholars assembled here. As I witness their successes, I see that it is possible to honor my community while exceeding academe's expectations. The academy is not a welcoming place for Black women, so we must move forward with confidence in spite of feeling uncovered. I am learning to negotiate all of the noise, lean on my mother and sister scholars, and retain my focus on *the work* to which I am called. As they stand, I learn to stand and reach out to support those to come.

Author 2's Counter-Story

When I was in eighth grade, I realized that I enjoyed mathematics and was good at it. Often tutoring my friends, I remember helping them to find common denominators and reduce fractions to simplest terms. Then in high school, I found myself experiencing anxiety in Algebra I class because my older brother earned Ds in the subject. To my surprise, however, Algebra was relatively easy for me with the exception of the occasional word problem about two trains moving in opposite directions or at different speeds. I earned A's in Algebra I and Algebra II/trigonometry but vowed never to take high school calculus because of the horror stories I heard from peers. Later in college, I took a survey of a calculus course. The professor was a woman. I found the course interesting and not too much of a challenge. I later enrolled in Calculus I and Calculus II/Analytical Geometry. Again, I had a female professor. I earned A's in both courses. Was it my ability, the fact that I had women instructors, or both that led to my success? These experiences led me to believe that gender and race matter in mathematics education.

The stereotype that women and African Americans are not as capable in mathematics as men and Asians is a myth (Steele, 2010; Stiff & Harvey, 1988). Stereotype threat impedes women and African Americans who believe the myth, which may cause them to feel anxiety and perform worse on standardized mathematics tests (Steele, 2010), creating a double bind in terms of race and gender. On the contrary, my performance in mathematics on standardized tests beginning with the Iowa Test of Basic Skills (ITBS) in eighth grade with a composite score of 12.1 in mathematics and

81st percentile in quantitative reasoning on the SAT and on the GMAT (I enrolled in an MBA program prior to obtaining a graduate degree in education) were impressive. My success in mathematics courses, scores on standardized tests, and self-efficacy, particularly in terms of vicarious experiences and verbal persuasion (Bandura, 1997) enabled me to believe I could not only do well in mathematics but also teach it effectively to others. In 1983, I became a mathematics specialist with Project SEED, Inc., in Dallas, Texas, where I taught algebra to underserved elementary students in the Dallas Independent School District (DISD). I also became a teacher leader and led several workshops for teachers in the DISD. It was particularly rewarding for teachers to enter my workshop with a look of resignation and newspaper and coffee in tow become totally engrossed in the activities. These direct, mastery experiences (Bandura, 1997) improved my self-efficacy enough to return to graduate school to earn a PhD in mathematics education armed with a passion to impact the efficacy and confidence of preservice teachers who were more likely to be women and doubt their mathematics ability.

However, my experiences as a female and African American assistant professor at a large urban university on the east coast were not what I expected. I recall vividly the reaction when I walked into the mathematics lab to teach my first mathematics methods course. The reaction was mixed as some White students dropped their jaws and others smiled and some African Americans exhaled a sigh of relief and others were ambivalent. Consistent with some research studies that revealed Blacks and Asians were evaluated more negatively than their White counterparts on overall quality and clarity (Reid, 2010), I struggled to prove my competence and credibility in the classroom. Students attended to every word that proceeded out of my mouth. When I made a mistake, even though I corrected myself, I could tell from the looks on some of their faces that I was confirming their doubts about my qualifications. Nevertheless, I drew upon my success as a teacher and won some of them over. Evaluations were lower if I talked about race, cultural relevance, and differences in learning styles with instructor effectiveness scores ranging as low as 3.25 on a five-point Likert scale. When I stopped talking about race and equity in my methods courses, evaluations ranged from 4.86 to a perfect score of 5.00 on overall instructor effectiveness. These results created a dilemma about how to best teach the methods courses. In the end, my decision was to stop talking about race until I obtained tenure.

At this point in my career, I have been tenured as a *professor* at three different predominantly White institutions. At the present time, I am one of six Black, female, full professors of mathematics education in the United States. Prior to 2010, this number was four. Such appallingly low numbers are indicative of the stress, rigor, and microaggressions that can be associated with the process. Although my case for promotion to full professor was tenuous, I prevailed. After nearly 20 years in higher education, my experience across the four institutions I have worked in can be narrowed down to one word—*respect*. Having written two books, more than 50 articles and book chapters, and garnering more than $6 million in research grants, people have to respect the work ethic. Such success cannot be happenstance. Yet, having traveled and presented across the globe, a *prophet* is without honor in her home institution. Nonetheless, I remain committed to teaching mathematics methods courses in academic settings where I can influence elementary and middle school teachers to teach mathematics for cultural relevance and social justice. My legacy is to give back to the communities that empowered me and to inspire the next generation of women and faculty of color in academe with the goal of doubling the number of Black women who are full professors of mathematics education in this decade.

Author 3's Counter-Story

I received tenure in the fall of 2013 and have remained at the same institution since I received my doctorate in 2006. Like most of my colleagues, I sit on a predominantly White faculty at an affluent, White institution. I have worked hard to position myself as a scholar and researcher at an institution that has traditionally favored teaching. While I am highly qualified to teach, during my pre-tenure years, I consciously resisted teaching multicultural education courses. I did not want to be pigeonholed and seen as capable only of teaching these kinds of courses. Instead of teaching these multicultural education courses, I took on research methods and mathematics methods courses, which serve large numbers of our students. These kinds of courses generally do not include any readings or assignments related to educational equity, class, race, gender, or multiculturalism. As lead instructor on these courses, I integrated these critical issues into general education courses and as such introduced a large range of students to these crucial issues. As I neared going up for tenure, I felt more comfortable and began teaching a social foundations course on educational equity. Like other faculty of color (particularly those on predominantly White campuses), I serve in numerous capacities on campus related to students of color, diversity, and so on. It can be overwhelming managing these commitments while at the same time conducting research and engaging in the larger work of educational equity. We have so much work to do as an African American community that the idea of seeking a full professorship seems ancillary to me. However, I recognize the startlingly low numbers of African American professors in mathematics education and know that gaining such a position is also important to our overall goals. I am learning to balance and beginning to recognize that I have been socialized to take the entire work of our community upon my own shoulders. As I move forward, I am keeping the important work of helping the African American community front and center, sharing my own struggles and triumphs with younger faculty members of color, and working to position myself for promotion to full professor in the coming years.

Author 4's Counter-Story

I was born and raised in the Southern United States, which has had a significant impact on my research and practice as a high school mathematics teacher and now as a tenured associate professor of mathematics education. The rich history of the South and its twinned heritage of discrimination and opportunity for Black Americans—rampant state-sanctioned segregation as well as strong communities of Black intellectuals, activists, educators, and leaders—continue to influence my work today. My schooling experiences with mathematics were largely positive—with the exception of one high school teacher who seemed surprised that one of the top students in his predominantly White mathematics class was a Black girl. The outstanding preparation I received in school settings—in the Atlanta public school system, in college, in graduate school—stands side by side with the high quality educational experiences I had outside of school settings, with my family, with teachers and community members, with other young people. These experiences within multiple settings along with my formal preparation in schools have been equally important to any claim I have to being a "math person," and have influenced how I teach, think about, and do mathematics and mathematics education research. Thus, when I walk in city neighborhoods or in the halls of urban schools, I do not see them as empty of promise, although there are plenty of stories about what these areas, their schools, and their students lack. I look for the talent that I know is there. When I look around our cities, I expect to see the same communities committed to young people's school and mathematics success. This perspective drives my work: to paint powerful pictures of how communities broadly support student success, and how policy and pedagogy shape the opportunity structures for underserved students in mathematics and can thwart or facilitate mathematical excellence.

I have been at the same institution as a postdoctoral fellow and as a faculty member in a great department for 13 years. My experiences at the institution have largely been positive, but they do mirror my experience throughout my schooling as being one of a few persons of color in STEM. For example, I was the only Black mathematics major at my undergraduate institution for some time, and now, I am the sole Black and sole female faculty member in mathematics education at my current institution. My research contributions have been valued, and I have strong, positive relationships with my colleagues and students. But as other faculty of color have reported, I am often called upon to support the institution in ways that others are not. For example, I have served on numerous committees, advised many students across the University, and spearheaded various initiatives. Fellow women of color at the institution—including Black women—report similar experiences. We are called upon to do more: to support and advise students both in and out of our departments and to represent "diversity" interests on committees and in meetings, for example. Such substantial service comes at a cost that others do not have to pay, and saying no is not always an option. There are moments when I think about how much more might have been accomplished during years when I had extremely heavy service commitments. Despite substantial service loads, my research efforts have been significant (including two single-authored books and numerous articles and book chapters). In my work, I draw on history and contemporary contexts to explore how people learn and are socialized to do mathematics in various "communities" (i.e., peer, neighborhood, school, family, and home). My own experiences in mathematics inspire me to dream of, work for, and enact better mathematics learning opportunities for everyone.

Analyses of Counternarratives

These four counter-narratives make plain the resilience and triumph amidst adversity that is the legacy of Black women in the United States. Although early and present obstacles could have derailed us from success as mathematics students, teachers, or teacher educators, we have repurposed those obstacles as motivators. Analysis of these counter-stories reveals four significant themes characteristic of Black women mathematics education faculty experiences: (a) expanding perspectives of promise in Black girls; (b) demanding respect through productivity; (c) negotiating institutional and personal values; and (d) recognizing the importance of woman instructors and mentors.

Expanding Perspectives of Promise in Black Girls

Each of us had very different early mathematics experiences—some more positive than others—but those experiences have brought each of us to a place where we see the mathematical promise in the Black girls who have been cast aside in mathematics classrooms. As Author 4 reflected, our experiences do not allow us to see only pathological despair in urban schools. Rather, we recognize the possibilities awaiting these children once granted the opportunity to learn. We are able to look into those classrooms and see ourselves in the eyes of young Black girls who, to others, may appear disconnected, disengaged, or incapable, and we refuse to allow those girls not to realize their mathematical potential.

Our roles as mathematics education faculty grant us a particular privilege to use our classrooms and our scholarship to make known the mathematical potential of Black girls, to equip teachers to respond to that potential, and to create knowledge that validates that potential. As mathematics education researchers, we use our scholarship to challenge dominant narratives of Black girls in mathematics, to highlight stories of successful Black women in mathematics, and to challenge mathematics education as a domain of whiteness and maleness (Martin, 2009, 2010). Our research builds a cadre of evidence contrary to dominant paradigms that undergird teachers like Author 1 who portrays a belief that Black girls who struggle with advanced mathematics do so because of "a basic lack of mathematical ability" (Secada, 1995, p. 157). We use our position as mathematics teacher educators to highlight the teacher's responsibility to create learning environments in which Black students see themselves as mathematical. We use readings and assignments in our classes that support our core beliefs that *all* students, regardless of race, class, and gender, can excel in mathematics if given the opportunity. Unfortunately, taking such a stance in the classroom is not without risk. Author 2 observed that, when she openly addressed issues of equity in her classes, her student evaluation scores were significantly lower than times when she did not.

Demanding Respect Through Productivity

"In order to be considered half as good, you have to work twice as hard." Most Black people are shaped in some way by this admonition, or something similar. We see excellence both as a mode of resistance and as insurance against presumptions of mediocrity (hooks, 2013). As Black women experiencing the double bind of racism and sexism in academe, we experience a need to use our productivity as a means to command respect from our colleagues, administrators, and institutions. External funding, peer-reviewed publications, national and international reputation, and teaching evaluations—in various proportions—are currency in the professoriate. It is the faculty member's burden to understand institutional priorities related to these elements and to shape her or his activities to meet those expectations. Evidence of race- and gender-based inequities and differential expectations related to service obligations and promotion and tenure decisions, combined with the fact that Black women have the lowest tenure-track retention rate (Sharpe & Swinton, 2012), present a compelling case for

Black women faculty to reach beyond stated expectations and "work twice as hard" to develop a modicum of security for promotion and tenure (see e.g., Cooper, 2006; Gregory, 2001; Rockquemore & Laszloffy, 2008; Thomas & Hollenshead, 2001).

Our counter-narratives provide further evidence that faculty women of color are presumed incompetent (Harris & González, 2012) and that such presumptions do not begin with the faculty experience or with promotion and tenure decisions. Author 1's story of a high school teacher who proposed that the solution to her challenges in advance mathematics was moving to a lower level course with other Black students instead of receiving additional support from the teacher is an example of early presumption of incompetence. As a junior faculty member, Author 3 chose to resist teaching courses grounded in multicultural education to avoid "being pigeonholed" in a way that diminishes her expertise in mathematics education. Black women faculty experience a fear of making mistakes or misspeaking in the classroom because, as Author 2 recounts, students use such mistakes as an opportunity to question the Black woman professor's knowledge and qualifications. These and other accounts positively exemplify Black women's persistence and resilience when facing attacks on our competence, but also raise physical and mental health concerns prompting calls for attention to self-care as a means to manage stress and to counter attempts at dehumanization (Cooke, 2014).

Negotiating Institutional and Personal Values

All of the counter-narratives reveal a tension between personal values and institutional values. Each of us negotiates these tensions in different ways based on our institution, experience, and career stage. In the pre-tenure stage, Author 1 must consider how to position herself in a way that honors both her sense of sacred responsibility (Dillard & Okpalaoka, 2011) to scholar-activism and the institution's values for scholarship. She must weigh each move in light of written and unwritten expectations that govern how pre-tenure faculty should write and speak (Onwuachi-Willig, 2012). Author 4 and Author 3's counter-narratives reveal similar challenges post-tenure. As the only Black female faculty member in mathematics education in her institution, Author 4's disproportionate local service obligations lead to reduced time and energy available for research, but she recognizes that these service opportunities allow her to have voice in decisions related to institutional diversity. Author 3 sees promotion to professor as "ancillary" to her larger goal of redressing educational inequity in the Black community. However, in light of the dearth of Black women professors in mathematics education that Author 2 also describes, she realizes that seeking promotion to professor is part of a related obligation "to change the face of the faculty" (Shields, 2012, p. 37). Therefore, she must continue to position herself to meet institutional expectations for this promotion. It would seem that, as a thrice-tenured professor, Author 2 would be in a position where her record would speak for itself, but she, too, must negotiate institutional politics to command respect.

Our experiences mirror those of other women faculty of color who must find balance "between choosing to give in to hierarchy and working the system" (Onwuachi-Willig, 2012, p. 143). Such balance requires maintaining impressions and interpersonal relationships so that other faculty members perceive us as hard working, competent, team players (Rockquemore & Laszloffy, 2008). Faculty women of color at all ranks have to measure a desire to challenge the establishment in the academy against a need to maintain employment and to scale the academic ladder and gain the privileges associated with higher ranks (Shields, 2012). Federal attention to STEM education has created significant opportunities for external funding (White House Office of Science and Technology Policy, 2012). These opportunities create particular institutional pressure for STEM education faculty to pursue these dollars. On one hand, women of color STEM education faculty are well-poised to seek such funding related to broadening participation in STEM. On the other hand, however, funding agencies are less likely to fund research efforts grounded in the qualitative, critical, feminist, and race-critical paradigms that female faculty of color are more likely to employ (Manna & Petrilli, 2008). In response, women faculty of color in STEM must consider ways to navigate the culture of institutional research while also pursuing research agendas that meet expectations for external funding support.

Recognizing the Importance of Women Instructors and Mentors

Stereotype threat related to race and gender causes girls of color to believe the mythology that they cannot perform well in mathematics (Steele, 2010). For those young women who make it through secondary mathematics and pursue undergraduate, graduate, and postgraduate STEM-related study, institutional support is a significant factor in their persistence (Perna et al., 2009). Formal institutional support structures are important but should exist *in addition to* the presence of women of color, teachers, and faculty in STEM-related courses. Author 2 recalls that her anxiety in mathematics courses seemed to lessen as she encountered female professors. For Author 1, a White woman teacher caused her to feel inferior in high school, while Black women faculty in her undergraduate institution helped her to build confidence in her ability as a student in mathematics and science. We all acknowledge that our presence in classrooms can have a similar effect for our female students.

The importance of support structures for women of color in STEM extends beyond the classroom into the professional space. In the academy, mentoring is an essential factor for success for women faculty of color (Cooper, 2006; Rockquemore & Laszloffy, 2008). Given all of the challenges facing Black female faculty in mathematics education, we rely on being mentors and seeking mentorship as an integral part of our success. For Author 2, achieving the highest faculty rank allows her "to inspire the next generation of women and faculty of color in academe" and to create opportunities for junior faculty. Author 4 and Author 3, as associate professors, have garnered sufficient experience to mentor junior faculty, yet continue to rely on the wisdom of more senior colleagues. Author 1, the most junior of the authors, relies heaviest on elder scholars but recognizes that she is responsible for continuing to build these support networks for those who follow.

Results and Significance

The results of this study are represented in four vignettes in which each Black female faculty member's (i.e., each author's) counter-narrative is told from a uniquely personal perspective. The counter-narratives address our mathematical histories and perspectives on navigating the academy, in general, and within the discipline of mathematics education, specifically. Age, location, and place spur different experiences that reveal a landscape of experience for Black women faculty in mathematics education that ranges from indifference to institutional support. Finally, we discuss modes of support that Black women faculty in mathematics education and STEM education writ large can engage to undergird each other across faculty ranks.

The four vignettes representing this study are part of a larger, compelling body of narratives of Black women faculty. While research literature about experiences of Black women faculty and Black women in STEM professions has begun to proliferate in recent years, this study takes a different turn to engage how Black female mathematics educators' mathematics experiences combine with their lived experiences of being Black and female to inform their research, teaching, and service. Additionally, this study uniquely addresses experiences across the career span and considers how Black female scholars can close ranks and engage generational strategies of support to encourage persistence and success for Black female mathematics education professors. The strikingly low number of Black female full professors in our field is shocking but challenges us to strive to change that statistic by mentoring and persevering despite personal setbacks. It is through such generational support that we can continue to reach our full potential and add strength to the community of STEM educators and STEM professionals.

REFERENCES

Bandura, A. (1997). *Self-efficacy: The exercise of control.* New York, NY: W. H. Freeman.

Collins, P. H. (2009). *Black feminist thought* (2nd ed.). New York, NY: Routledge.

Cooke, N. A. (2014). Pushing back from the table: Fighting to maintain my voice as a pre-tenure minority female in the white academy. *Polymath an Interdisciplinary Journal of Arts Sciences, 4*(2), 39–49.

Cooper, T. L. (2006). *The sista' network: African-American women faculty successfully negotiating the road to tenure.* Boston, MA: Anker.

Delgado, R. (2012). *Critical race theory* (2nd ed.). New York, NY: New York University Press.

Dillard, C. B. (2000). The substance of things hoped for, the evidence of things not seen: Examining an endarkened feminist epistemology in educational research and leadership. *International Journal of Qualitative Studies in Education, 13*(6), 661–681.

Dillard, C. B., & Okpalaoka, C. (2011). The sacred and spiritual nature of endarkened transnational feminist praxis in qualitative research. In N. K. Denzin & Y. S. Lincoln, *The SAGE handbook of qualitative research* (pp. 147–162). Los Angeles, CA: SAGE.

Gregory, S. T. (2001). Black faculty women in the academy: History, status, and future. *The Journal of Negro Education, 70*(3), 124–138.

Harris, A. P., & González, C. G. (2012). Introduction. In G. Gutiérrez y Muhs, Y. F. Niemann, C. G. González, & A. P. Harris, *Presumed incompetent: The intersections of race and class for women in academia* (pp. 1–14). Boulder: University Press of Colorado.

Holt, N. (2003). Representation, legitimation, and autoethnography: An autoethnographic writing story. *International Journal of Qualitative Methods, 2*(1), 2–22.

hooks, B. (2013). *Writing beyond race: Living theory and practice.* New York, NY: Routledge.

Manna, P., & Petrilli, M. J. (2008). Double standard? "Scientifically based research" and the No Child Left Behind Act. In F. M. Hess (Ed.), *When research matters: How scholarship influences education policy* (pp. 63–88). Cambridge, MA: Harvard Education Press.

Martin, D. B. (2009). Researching race in mathematics education. *Teachers College Record, 111*(2), 295–338.

Martin, D. B. (2010). Not-so-strange bedfellows: Racial projects and the mathematics education enterprise. In U. Gellert, E. Jablonka, & C. Morgan (Eds.), *Proceedings of the xixth International Mathematics Education and Society conference* (Vol. 1; pp. 42–64). Berlin, Germany: Freie Universität Berlin.

Onwuachi-Willig, A. (2012). Silence of the lambs. In G. Gutiérrez y Muhs, Y. F. Niemann, C. G. González, & A. P. Harris (Eds.), *Presumed incompetent: The intersections of race and class for women in academia* (pp. 142–151). Boulder: University Press of Colorado.

Perna, L. W., Lundy-Wagner, V., Drezner, N. D., Gasman, M., Yoon, S., Bose, E., & Gary, S. (2009). The contribution of HBCUs to the preparation of African American women for STEM careers: A case study. *Research in Higher Education, 50*(1), 1–23.

Phillips, L., & McCaskill, B. (1995). Who's schooling who? Black women and the bringing of the everyday into academe, or why we started 'The Womanist'. *Signs: Journal of Women in Culture and Society, 20*(4), 1007–1018.

Reid, L. D. (2010). The role of perceived race and gender in the evaluation of college teaching on ratemyprofessors.com. *Journal of Diversity in Higher Education, 3*(3), 137–152.

Rockquemore, K. A., & Laszloffy, T. (2008). *The black academic's guide to winning tenure—without losing your soul.* Boulder, CO: Lynne Rienner.

Secada, W. G. (1995). Social and critical dimensions for equity in mathematics education. In W. G. Secada, E. Fennema, & L. B. Adajian (Eds.), *New directions for equity in mathematics education* (pp. 146–164). Cambridge, England: Cambridge University Press.

Sharpe, R. V., & Swinton, O. H. (2012). Beyond anecdotes: A quantitative examination of Black women in academe. *The Review of Black Political Economy, 39*(3), 341–352.

Shields, S. A. (2012). Waking up to privilege: Intersectionality and opportunity. In G. Gutiérrez y Muhs, Y. F. Niemann, C. G. González, & A. P. Harris (Eds.), *Presumed incompetent: The intersections of race and class for women in academia* (pp. 29–39). Boulder: University Press of Colorado.

Solórzano, D. G., & Yasso, T. J. (2002). Critical race methodology: Counter-storytelling as an analytical framework for education research. *Qualitative Inquiry, 8*(1), 23–44.

Steele, C. M. (2010). *Whistling Vivaldi: How stereotypes affect us and what we do.* New York, NY: Norton.

Stiff, L., & Harvey, W. B. (1988). On the education of Black children in mathematics. *Journal of Black Studies, 19*(2), 190–203.

Thomas, G. D., & Hollenshead, C. (2001). Resisting from the margins: The coping strategies of Black women and other women on color faculty members at a research university. *The Journal of Negro Education, 70*(3), 166–175.

Van Manen, M. (1990). *Researching lived experience: Human science for an action sensitive pedagogy.* Albany: State University of New York Press.

White, E. F. (2001). *Dark continent of our bodies: Black feminism and the politics of respectability.* Philadelphia, PA: Temple University Press.

White House Office of Science and Technology Policy. (2012). *Preparing a 21st century workforce: Science, technology, engineering, and mathematics (STEM) education in the 2013 budget.* Retrieved from https://obamawhitehouse.archives.gov/sites/default/files/microsites/ostp/fy2013rd_stem.pdf

CHAPTER 5

COLORFUL PORTRAITS OF SUCCESS

Black Women With Doctorates in Science, Technology, Engineering, or Mathematics (STEM)

Virginia C. Tickles
Krystal A. Foxx

Booker T. Washington (1901) proclaimed, "Success is to be measured not so much by the position one has reached in life, as by the obstacles which one has overcome while trying to succeed" (p. 22). Frederick Douglass said, "If there is no struggle, there is no progress." (Douglas & Garrison, 1849, p. 1.). According to Kimbro (2006), success is an attitude, a matter of choice, and the positive results of the pursuit of a goal. It demands learning and growing; and requires faith, commitment, and permanence. Success also demands the use of available talents and abilities (Kimbro, 2006). More specifically, career success in this chapter is defined as the combination of achievements and experiences that made obtaining a doctoral degree in the STEM discipline

Women of Color In STEM, pages 71–89
Copyright © 2021 by Information Age Publishing
All rights of reproduction in any form reserved.

possible, as well as continuous commitment in the STEM workforce providing technical input and support to scientific research.

An example of the career success for Black Women in STEM can be similar to the career path of Mae Jemison, a physician, scientist, and engineer, who was the first Black female to go into space (Feinstein, 2003; Jordan, 2006; Perna et al., 2009). Or, success can be described by the career path of Ruth Ella Moore, the first Black female to earn a PhD in bacteriology (Warren, 1999). There are other pioneers of success, such as Willie Hobbs Moore who graduated from the University of Michigan as the first Black woman to earn a PhD in physics in the United States, and Martha Euphemia Lofton Haynes who in 1943 was the first Black Woman to earn a PhD in mathematics (Jordan, 2006). All of these women chose STEM careers and made valuable contributions through their successful accomplishments.

However, it's quite visible that Black women are poorly represented in the STEM disciplines (Hegewisch & Hartmann, 2014; Landivar, 2013; Ong, Wright, Espinosa, & Orfield, 2011; Perna et al., 2009). Ethnic-racial groups and women continue to be underrepresented at higher education institutions, and women generally continue to be outnumbered in upper-level positions in the STEM workforce (Hill, Corbett, & St. Rose, 2010). Many still believe that women, particularly Black women, lack the ability to achieve in the STEM fields (National Science Board, 2006), but researchers have shown that the representation of women in STEM occupations has increased since the 1970s even though they still remain underrepresented (Landivar, 2013; Ong, Wright, Espinosa, & Orfield, 2011). Researchers also have revealed that women that are less satisfied in the academic workplace are less likely to stay in STEM careers if they feel that they are less likely to advance within their career. The problem of the shortage of Black women in technically advanced careers does not just show its face in the classroom. Black women experience a high rate of turnover and field switching in the technical workforce compared to other groups (Prince, 2013; The Mendoza Commission, 2000; Turk-Bicakci & Berger, 2014). These occurrences are related directly to biases that exist in the workforce, such as the lack of equitable pay and promotion rates; the absence of adequate mentoring; exclusion from informal networks, both internally and externally; minimum management opportunities; and difficulties in balancing work and family life (Prince, 2013; Takihara, Goodings, & Byrnes, 1998). These disparities are similar for doctoral level Black female scientists and engineers.

Workplace cultures are being challenged to change in order to correct for the differences in individual cultures, genders, and socioeconomic backgrounds as it relates to individuals in the STEM workforce (Prince, 2013; The Mendoza Commission, 2000). Black women in these fields have difficulty adapting and coping with this male-oriented culture. The lack of self-confidence in these situations prohibit Black women from achieving their full potential as they are constantly being challenged to provide a balance between family commitments and career goals (Birch et al., 2002). Wulf (1999) speculated that increasing the number of women and other minority groups in engineering would result in increased workplace productivity as women provide a totally different and creative perspective from than their male counterparts. These beliefs contribute greatly to the reason why the lack of Black women in STEM continues to gain worldwide attention. Thus, it is important to understand from an economics standpoint that science and engineering graduates with advanced degrees are vital for America to secure its position as a world leader in technology (Oakes, Mccomb, Mulkay, Berger, Blevins, Stamber, & Jones, 1999; Prince, 2013; Slaughter & McPhail, 2007).

STEM fields have been responsible for providing approximately 50% of the United States' economic growth for the past 50 years in areas such as education, research, and employment (Malcolm, Chubin, & Jesse, 2004). However, statistics indicate that in 2011, women made up only 26% of those in STEM careers, and underrepresented ethnic-racial groups made up roughly 17% with even less of a percentage being women of color (Landivar, 2013). In engineering, 9,582 doctorates were awarded to Americans in 2011 (Yoder, 2011). Of those, 21.8% were received by women and only 59 Black women received their doctorates (Yoder, 2011). In 2010, 6,400 women of color (even less for Black women) with STEM doctorates held assistant, associate, or full professorships while 19,800 White women, 20,500 men of color, and 65,100 White men (Prince, 2013). These statistics are alarming and require significant changes to increase STEM graduates of color, particularly Black women, since the majority of the United States will be persons of color in 2043 (United States Census Bureau, 2012).

Women who persevere to receive a doctorate in a technical field are usually considered extremely talented and persistent as there are so many places that they can "leak out of the pipeline" (Jordan, 2006; Zurk, Simons, Parsons, & Cohen, 1995). These women frequently struggle to break through various barriers such as constantly enduring the questioning of their statements, opinions, and decisions; working harder to receive technical and professional credibility; shouldering the multifaceted issues of domestic life; and contending with a glass ceiling (Jordan, 2006; Zurk et al., 1995). They have to constantly convince themselves and others that they deserve the recognition they receive (Jordan, 2006; Zurk et al., 1995). These gendered barriers present roadblocks to success and create environments where they constantly deal with issues of workplace inequalities (Powell, Bagihole, & Dainty, 2009; Rhoton, 2011; Xu, 2013).

Throughout history, there have been and will continue to be Black women pioneers whose courage, hard work, and dedication have created space for many others to make a difference. These Black women possess tremendous character, persistence, and talent and have a deep commitment to science and tremendous personal discipline (Jordan, 2006; MacLachlan, 2000). Therefore, the need to understand and increase diversity in both STEM higher education and the workforce is important to continue innovative productivity from people of diverse backgrounds and experiences to remain a global contender with other countries (Corbett & Hill 2015; Prince, 2013; Slaughter & McPhail, 2007).

FACTORS AFFECTING DEGREE ATTAINMENT

There are many factors that affect Black women obtaining degrees and working in a STEM environment. Age, marital status, number of children, goals/attitudes, type of institution, grade point average (GPA), relationships with instructors, satisfaction with the course of study, and financial stability are just a few. Jordan (2006) described women's ongoing and disproportionate family responsibilities as limiting to their ability to compete in science fields. Sax (1996) reports that women who place a high priority on children and family life will likely experience greater difficulty while pursuing doctoral degrees in science, mathematics, and engineering and are less likely to enter nontraditional academic majors. Evidence tends to indicate that family obligations affect women differently than men especially in the transition from obtaining their doctorates to full-time employment in the scientific and engineering labor force.

Race and gender have a negative impact on the work experiences and career advancement of Black women (Bell & Nkomo, 2001; Combs, 2003; Hegewisch & Hartmann, 2014). In the workforce, women experience bigger problems on the job including job stability, job satisfaction, gender segregation, promotion, adequate mentors, career changes, exclusion from informal networks, and family responsibility (Hegewisch & Hartmann, 2014; Prince, 2013; Takihara et al., 1998). Historically there has been a limited supply of female role models as educators have failed to nurture and mentor young Black women (Borum & Walker, 2012; Brown, Brown, Reardon, & Merrill, 2011; Jordan, 2006; Warren, 1999). Karet (1999) expresses that mentors are vital for navigating and understanding the politics and providing an avenue for making the work of Black women in STEM areas much more visible.

Long (2001) discusses the principle of a triple penalty that exists for women scientists, which include having to (a) overcome barriers to enter STEM fields, (b) deal with perceived discrimination as it relates to limited aspirations, and (c) deal with actual discrimination in opportunities and rewards. Mabokela and Green (2001) discussed a similar concept of triconsciousness of lived experiences explained by being a Black woman, being a woman in a male-dominated environment, and the inequities in the

Black community. Understanding the experiences of female scientists and engineers can perpetuate improvement in the work and educational environment and increase participation of women in male dominated fields (Corbett & Hill, 2015; Moskal, 2000). Therefore, we delve into the experiences of Black women to understand how to further shape STEM education and the workplace to increase participation of underrepresented groups.

THEORETICAL FRAMEWORK

There is a "theoretical silence" about the success of Black women and the extra demands imposed on them. Black women are described as extremely unique and pay a social price for success (Martin, 1999) in having to overcome many of the barriers that deter them from careers in science, technology, engineering, and mathematics. They have sought education in these fields and have achieved at the highest attainable level. Who better than they to express the elements of success as viewed through their personal experiences?

To further understand the experiences of Black women in STEM, Black feminist thought is a useful theory that allow the researchers to delve into the meaning of those lived experiences, especially as it relates to race, class, sexual orientation, and national origin (Collins, 2000; Crenshaw, 1995; hooks, 2000; Springer, 2005). *Being the only one* in the workplace, which is the case for many Black women in STEM, are one of several conditions that allows the lens of Black feminist thought to prevail in this study. Additionally, social cognitive career theory (SCCT; Lent, Brown, & Hackett, 1994), which expands from Albert Bandura's social cognitive theory, serves as a theoretical lens for this study. SCCT concentrates on how social support and social barriers impact academic and career attitudes and behaviors and aims to explain how academic and career choices are made based on environmental (barriers and support), personal, and behavioral traits (Fleming, Moore, Williams, Bliss, & Smith, 2013). The merging of these two theories is highlighted as the guiding frameworks for this qualitative study.

METHODS

The qualitative method of analysis in this chapter interprets the responses to face-to-face interviews of six Black women holding doctorates in STEM disciplines, for the purpose of exploring the factors that impacted their career success and the commonalities of their experiences. The women interviewed in this study all identify with being Black and have PhDs in a STEM field (four physics, two engineering). Five attained their degrees at a historically Black college and university (HBCU) and one at a predominantly

White institution (PWI). All six women at the time of this study were employed in the STEM workforce as physicists and engineers and were selected based on accessibility to the researchers. Pseudonyms given for the participants are Anita, Belinda, Connie, Denise, Elaine, and Felecia.

The interview protocol included five open-ended statements or talking points for the purposes of allowing the participant to provide in-depth details of experiences that molded their career successes as well as demographic data. The data obtained from the interview process was collected using the appropriate IRB requirements and answers the question, "Are there similarities in the career success experiences (knowledge, behaviors, and attitudes) of Black women with doctorates in STEM that provide insight into what helps/hinders their progress?"

This qualitative research embraces a phenomenological design to understand the basic elements of the lived experience (Creswell, 2013). Phenomenology allows small samples of participants with direct experiences with the phenomenon (Creswell, 2013; Leedy & Omrod, 2001). The data, once collected, was evaluated in search of emerging themes and then coded while also ensuring the quality and integrity of the data obtained (reliability; Creswell, 2013). The emerging themes were assembled and supported by narratives with thick descriptions provided by the participants and are discussed below.

EMERGING THEMES OF SUCCESS OF BLACK WOMEN IN STEM

Analysis of the data reveals similarities in the career success experiences of the Black women in this study that provide insight into what helped them to progress through their STEM discipline. These emerging themes are spirituality, a passion for math and/or science, positive attitudes and behaviors, and mentorship/family support.

Spirituality

The women in this study agreed unanimously that a belief in a spiritual presence, which they identified as God, was vital in their ability to survive and excel in science- and engineering-related educational and workplace environments. All of them recalled moments of prayer and jubilation when their prayers were met. Statements supporting these findings were:

> I know it was the grace of God, having paid my dues and proven again and again that I knew my material. (Felecia)

That [the struggles] was God keeping me from getting other things and not accepting that I had been defeated. (Anita)

I remember I was praying and I couldn't take it anymore. (Elaine)

When asked about how to improve the climate for Black women in this environment, Denise replied, "You mean other than prayer?" These women held steadfastly to a strong spiritual belief in God as motivation to continue on their journey as they pioneered their way through the science and engineering roadblocks.

Passion for Math and/or Science

Every participant in this study understood the importance of a strong math and science background as the fundamental pattern of knowledge that they must possess. Another commonality of experiences for the women in this study was that each had a passion for math and/or science. All expressed a love for math and/or science in an effort to understand how and why things work.

I chose physics because it was challenging and I loved math and science. (Belinda)

My first influence with physics and engineering came from watching Star Trek. (Denise)

I went into engineering because I like the math and it offered a very good income potential. (Elaine)

In essence, everyone made it clear from their experiences that there has to be an appreciation for math or science to be able to survive the requirements of the STEM environment. Even so, some of the women in this study acknowledged the difficulty in the subject matter. Elaine states, "I did not have the requisite physics and mathematics background to undertake the engineering curriculum; however, I chose to stay the course." Though she expressed difficulties in the math and science subject matter, it was clear that she understood what it would take to persist.

Positive Attitudes and Behaviors

Common amongst all participants was positive attitudes and behaviors that must be demonstrated in order to gain access to the path of success. Participants made comments such as:

> Always keep a good attitude . . . do the things you're supposed to and make sure you're capable and well-prepared. (Connie)

> You have to know that you've done your personal best! (Felecia)

The attitudes and behaviors of (a) having determination, persistence, and hard work; (b) being optimistic and seeking opportunities; (c) exhibiting professionalism; (d) displaying competence; and (e) demonstrating self-awareness emerged as sub-themes for having overall positive attitudes and behaviors. These subthemes, discussed further below, provided a more in-depth analysis of the experiences faced in both the educational and workplace environments in STEM.

Determination, Persistence, and Hard Work

Responses supporting the subtheme relative to attitudes of determination, persistence, and hard work are mentioned below.

> They try to make it extremely hard for us, but if you're a woman in a male-dominated field, you have to be determined and not give up. (Belinda)

> Working hard and seeing that hard work paid off. (Denise)

> You can't quit because you never know how close you are to finishing. (Elaine)

Felecia recalled a professor stating that she would never be successful. Relative to his comments she said, "It [professor's comment] gave me more determination to keep going to show him that women can succeed." Felecia further commented by stating, "He gave me determination to do better and those experiences were what actually helped me to achieve my goals. You have to be willing to put forth effort, good effort; then you'll be successful at anything you do."

Seeking Opportunities

Another subtheme revealed by the women in this study is the importance of seeking other opportunities when efforts to advance have stalled. Participants stated:

> What I would do is seek out opportunities to do different types of things. If you're not happy with where you are, find a place where you can be happy . . . happy about being properly utilized. (Connie)

> I think that Black women can improve their own situations by realizing that they may have to be as mobile as NASA's Dr. Mae Jemison in order to avoid the racism traps of staying in one place too long. (Elaine)

> Don't look at a door that is closed as a closed door, but instead a door that God hasn't had the opportunity to open because you're not ready to go

through it, but when he's ready for you to go through it you have step up to the plate. (Felecia)

The participants in this study recognized many of the roadblocks and understood that sometimes moving to other organizations or finding other opportunities were necessary to continue towards their ultimate goal of career success.

Exhibiting Professionalism

The subtheme of exhibiting professionalism was revealed from several of the STEM women with PhDs interviewed for this study. They also revealed the necessity of displaying *professionalism* in the work environment no matter what the situation.

> Always present yourself professionally. When we walk in a room it is assumed that we need to be somewhere else ... you have to watch how you carry yourself. We have to watch what we say, not that we can't say things or express our minds, but we have to be real tactful or a deaf ear falls upon you. We can't change people, but we can change how they see us. (Denise)

> The more prepared and vigilant we are in making sure we take an active interest in other Blacks in the workplace, the more professional we are at work ... We are expected to use Ebonics, to roll our neck and eyes in meetings and act less than professional. You have to display professionalism at work. (Felecia)

In essence, it was revealed that no matter the "chilly climate," one must be mindful of their own professionalism to improve the climate for women in STEM and progress accordingly.

Displaying Competence

The subtheme of displaying competence was also revealed from participants of the study. Specifically, participants stated:

> You have to know that you know that you know ... and I learned everything I could about any project in and out. Then at the right time, I said the right things. (Felecia)

> I had something he [another supervisor] needed or wanted ... he's not going to say he needs your expertise. (Anita)

The participants of this study noted the hard work and dedication needed to get to a level of competency but understood that it was vital to getting to a point of success in their career. Getting to the point of being valued for what they brought to the table was fundamental to their career success.

Demonstrating Self-Awareness

The subtheme of demonstrating self-awareness was also revealed in the study by the participants. Participants were aware of the environment and how they were perceived as women as they pursued their STEM doctoral education and navigated the workforce. Some of their responses included:

> If we are aware of the fact that where we're going may not always want us to be there and not be disillusioned . . . be prepared for it. (Connie)

> It's not a panacea . . . when you get to the top of the plateau, you realize it's not what you thought . . . so you really have to know who you are before you get there. (Elaine)

> "You have to realize where you are, and what the perceptions and expectations are of women," disclosed another participant when asked about changing the climate. (Felecia)

For the participants in this study, self-awareness is deemed vital in helping to improve the climate by changing the culture for women in STEM.

MENTORSHIP AND FAMILY SUPPORT

Experiences related to mentorship and family support also were prevalent in the ability to assist and encourage Black women in STEM-related educational and workplace environments. All of the women provided continuous stories of supportive parents who motivated them to succeed. Stories of relentless attitudes of mentors providing the necessary methods of encouragement and teachers and instructors who understood the process and knew what it would take to navigate the STEM environment were also provided. Statements from the interviews supporting this finding are listed below.

> My family was my greatest inspiration and encouragement, and My mentor, a renowned physicist tore up my first thesis in my face because he said he doesn't take junk. It was his brute force method that helped me realize that I wasn't where I needed to be and gave me the determination to do better. (Felecia)

> I was encouraged by another professor. He watched my career progress and encouraged me. It was him [professor] in my life making me push farther and farther, making me strive to do better and better in my career field. (Felecia)

> He [my mentor] saw something in me as a Black woman and challenged me to do my absolute best and to always operate in a spirit of excellence. (Denise)

> My parents' motto was "Go as high as you can, get all you can, while you can." (Denise)

This finding supports the research that shows that mentorship for women of color in STEM has been known to be an effective strategy for aiding in the personal and academic success of women who navigate through academia and in STEM disciplines (Amelink, 2009).

CHALLENGES TO SUCCESS OF BLACK WOMEN IN STEM

The commonality in the experiences of the participants in this study revealed challenges that Black women experience while seeking STEM success. Issues of race and gender, lack of opportunities, educational and workplace politics, and feelings of disillusionment were all emerging themes revealed as hindrances to success.

Race and Gender

All of the women recalled negative comments coming from mostly White male colleagues in the educational and workplace environment. Statements and observations supporting this theme are:

> They scrutinize your work harder than they would a male. (Elaine)

> Engineering is not a field for women, and you will never be successful. (Felecia)

> This is a new field for women, especially Black women. There's no standard to compare them to in this field. Maybe when more of them enter the field, we'll have more to compare them to. (Connie)

The participants in this study are aware that race and gender issues are prevalent in many places in this world. However, its impact in the STEM environment has a negative impact on the success of Black women in STEM.

Lack of Opportunities

The majority of these women discussed hindrances in their careers relative to a lack of opportunities. More specifically, the lack of being assigned challenging work, a lack of direction, being passed over for promotions and raises, and inadequate starting salaries surfaced. Belinda states, "A lot of times we're hired in; nobody trains you; you're expected to perform, and they leave you by yourself and forget you're there. As Blacks, we have been the people that have been left behind." Belinda further states:

I don't want a promotion, what I want is challenging work, and my work will speak for me, and eventually I'll earn that promotion. I have to work twice as hard as my white male counterparts; I have to fight for challenging work, and I have to demand respect based on my merit. I don't want to be a value to the group because I am a black female; I want my value to be what I bring to the table in expertise and knowledge. (Belinda)

While these experiences are roadblocks and sometimes discourage and deter Black women from continuing in these areas, these women made it clear that those roadblocks were not insurmountable to them and they were there to stay.

Educational and Workplace Politics

Educational politics relative to dealing with advisors also proved to be hindrances in achieving success in the male-dominated culture of engineering and science. At least three women had difficulty dealing with issues of politics and power of male advisors in the educational environment.

I had to learn the politics to do what the advisor said do, no matter how difficult or how much . . . he had to show me what I had to do. He would change the rules; he would tell you to go get a blue dog, and when you do, he would say that's not the color blue I wanted. (Elaine)

It was challenging trying to satisfy both advisors, as they didn't always see eye to eye, but we worked through it. (Connie)

Workplace politics was another area that was strong in its ability to discourage or hinder progress in a STEM discipline. They all agreed that as Black women, they had to learn the "rules of the game," or they would not survive.

It's not personal; it's just business . . . they say it's a dog eat dog world, but it's a male dog eat dog world, and all of the male dogs get together to attack when you're a black female. (Elaine)

It takes a while before they (white males) feel comfortable enough with you to give you those things that will challenge you. (Connie)

The big thing with working with all males is you can play ball with them but when you do, you have to understand the game they are playing . . . the rules are not always the same. (Felecia)

The participants' understanding and perceptions of the political nature of the science and engineering environment relative to Black women's entrance and persistence resolve to accept that navigating this journey in the STEM culture would be difficult.

Feelings of Disillusionment

The feeling of disillusionment emerged as a theme that hindered success. However, disillusionment in some cases was a turning point for at least two of the women. They recalled reaching the point where they considered giving up on obtaining their doctorate degree.

> I remembered praying; and I couldn't take it anymore to the point that I would rather quit. . . . and my mentor said, if you quit for the right reason, 5 years from now it won't matter but, if you quit for the wrong reasons, 5 years from now you'll kick yourself every time you think about it. (Elaine)

> My chairman had to tell me not to let someone change my goals and I had to once again decide that I wasn't starting over. (Anita)

The commonality of the experiences of these six women provides insight into what hinders the progress of career success of Black women in STEM environments. Though these hindrances delayed the progress, participants were able to overcome and in many instances use those as motivation to continue their journey.

ANALYSIS OF FINDINGS

There are various paths to career success; however, these Black women, in many ways experienced very similar paths along the way. To describe the commonalities of career success of Black women in a STEM discipline the Y symbol is being used, extracted from a comment made by one of the participants as she described her navigation in STEM:

> If there's a Y in the road, there's left or right and if you go right don't be discouraged if something doesn't happen the way you thought it should. You have to have a determined mind, and you have to know that you're doing the right thing. You have to be willing to sometimes settle for what you don't deserve. A lot of times you will be disappointed. You can't be too big to know that you can't always be seen as the best nor can you always satisfy somebody else's expectations or you're not going to be successful. You have to know that what you've done is your personal best, because there are people who won't like anything that you do. You can't live for other people. Some people you can never make them happy no matter what. You have to know that, and to have that type of spirit, you have to be willing to go the extra mile. If you're

willing to put forth effort, good effort, then you'll be successful at anything you do. (Felecia)

Career success for Black women with STEM PhDs depicted by the symbolic Y in Figure 5.1 displays the findings that most of these Black women, upon entering the educational process brought certain characteristics with them: spirituality, math and science interests, various avenues of support from family, mentors and friends, and their own unique attitudes. "Black women bring a unique blend of culture, strength, courage, character, and outstanding skills and analytical abilities to the table" (Jordan, 2006, p. 26). As these women started their journey, their insistence in reaching their goals birthed other factors; building a strong math and science background, becoming competent, building self-awareness, displaying professionalism, seeking opportunities for advancement, and displaying characteristics of determination and hard work.

As these Black women continued to venture up the road towards career success, all had plans as to how they would get there. However, along the road came the various obstacles in one form or another that they had to overcome to reach their goals. Those obstacles were issues related to race and gender, lack of performance opportunities, educational and workplace politics, and feelings of disillusionment. All are very complex and interwoven within one another. Jordan (2006) describes these feelings below:

> There are times when only another Black woman scientist can possibly understand the dilemma...I know these women's voices. I know their joys; I know

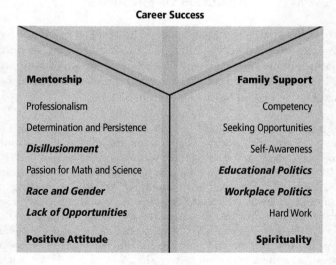

Figure 5.1   Common career success attributes for STEM doctoral Black women.

their pain. I know their triumphs; I know their despair; I know these women and they know me. We share a form of marginalization that others find difficult to grasp and that we often have a hard time expressing in terms that others really understand. (p. 230)

Jordan (2006) also explains, "This is the point at which 'we look beyond each other's race, gender, and class. It is looking beyond those external factors that allowed all of us to break barriers'" (p. 231).

The very nature of career success requires the achievement of a balance in personal beliefs and experiences, educational experiences, and workplace experiences in the lives of these women. More specifically, these attributes consist of having a strong faith, having supportive friends, family, role models, mentors and advisors, possessing a passion or love for the field, displaying positive attitudes and behaviors, being competent, and embracing a supportive educational and workplace culture.

DISCUSSION AND IMPLICATIONS

We provide reflections of the experiences of six Black women with doctorates in a STEM field. Through the lens of Black feminist thought and social cognitive career theory, the Black women in this study were able to provide candid accounts of how they view their career success which is supported by relevant literature. In doing so, the analysis of these findings helps to document the commonalities of their struggle to achieve success. This in turn can serve as a platform for improving the climate for women in these fields. Stories of how Black women in a science, technology, engineering, and mathematics (STEM) discipline obtained their doctorate degree and how they navigated in a highly White, male-dominated field were revealed. Descriptions of what it is like to work and succeed in the STEM environment as well as accounts of how women juggle family, spirituality, and social affairs with educational and career goals were revealed. Ultimately, how these women view their career success became apparent and will serve to provide valuable insight for Black women who seek careers and doctoral degrees in a STEM discipline. Through this proposed chapter, personal experiences/ stories and recommendations have been shared with the hopes that the intended audience can develop strategies to move forward the agenda of diversity and the need to increase the number of women in STEM.

Several themes emerged to support the concept of a common ground amongst the experiences of Black women in STEM. First, spirituality was identified as being at the core of their success. Second, the support of family, friends, role models, mentors, teachers, professors and advisors was identified as being crucial to the road of success, with both a negative and positive impact. Third, each woman's internal desire was to succeed and the unique personality traits and behaviors that they possessed, such as a love for the discipline/field, determination, and a positive attitude to bring about change in both the educational climate and workplace culture. Fourth, self-knowledge of the environment and the opportunities that exist in the environment were vital to help avoid issues of race and gender for prolonged periods of time and prevent the overwhelming feeling of disillusionment that also emerged as the last theme.

All of these concepts define the common ground of career success of women of the Black race, who persevered, despite the odds, and excelled to the highest attainable level (doctorate degree) in their chosen STEM field. Based on the themes identified by the participants, some important factors that play a major role in a STEM environment include continuously exceeding workplace expectations, establishing a reputation of dependability and competence, and maintaining and developing positive attitudes and behaviors when dealing with the current issues in the workplace. This chapter will be helpful in assisting policymakers and program designers in creating a conducive workplace and educational environment for all STEM workers, regardless of the race or gender. Additionally, this information is useful for improving the participation of Black women in STEM education and careers.

Researchers should further explore the role that culture plays in career success of Black women with STEM doctorates using frameworks of cultural empowerment theories. Additionally, the differences in educational backgrounds and experiences (e.g., HBCUs, HSIs, PWIs) should be explored to examine how those experiences have shaped Black women's leadership through their STEM careers. These future implications will be vital for understanding how women of color, particularly Black women, can utilize their personal and professional strengths to mentor others and create a better climate in the workplace.

REFERENCES

Amelink, C. (2009). *Overview: Mentoring and women in engineering.* Retrieved from http://aweonline.org/arp_mentoring_overview120408_003.pdf

Bell, E. D. T, & Nkomo, S. (2001). *Our separate ways: Black and White women and the struggle for professional identity.* Boston, MA: Harvard University Press.

Birch, M., Gibbs, B., Hanson, J., Nedwell, J.C., Porter, V.A., & Waters, B. (2002). *Mentoring women in science, engineering and technology in higher education.* London, England: The Institution of Electrical Engineers.

Borum V., & Walker, E. (2012). What makes the difference? Black women's undergraduate and graduate experiences in mathematics. *The Journal of Negro Education, 81*(4), 366–378.

Brown, R., Brown, J., Reardon, K., & Merrill, C. (2011). Understanding STEM: Current perceptions. *Technology and Engineering Teacher, 70*(6), 5–9.

Collins, P. H. (2000). *Black feminist thought: Knowledge, consciousness, and the politics of empowerment.* New York, NY: Routledge

Combs, G. M. (2003). The duality of race and gender for managerial African American women: Implications of informal social networks on career advancement. *Human Resource Development Review, 2*(4), 385–405.

Corbett, C., & Hill, C. (2015) *Solving the equation: The variables for women's success in engineering and computing.* Washington, DC: American Association of Women.

Crenshaw, K. W. (1995). Mapping the margins: Intersectionality, identity politics, and violence against women of color. In K. Crenshaw, N. Gotanda, G. Peller, K. Thomas (Eds.), *Critical race theory: The key writings that informed the movement* (pp. 357–383). New York, NY: The New Press.

Creswell, J. W. (2013). *Qualitative inquiry & research design: Choosing among five approaches* (3rd ed.). Thousand Oaks, CA: SAGE.

Douglass, F., & Garrison, W. L. (1849). *Narrative of the life of Frederick Douglass, an American slave.* Boston, MA: Anti-Slavery Office. Retrieved from https://www.loc.gov/item/82225385/

Hill, C., Corbett, C., & St. Rose, A. (2010). *Why so few? Women in science, technology, engineering, and mathematics.* Washington, DC: American Association of University Women.

hooks, b. (2000). *Feminist theory: From margin to center.* Cambridge, MA: South End Press.

Feinstein, D. (2003). *The measure of success: Celebrating a legacy of African American achievement.* U.S. Senator Dianne Feinstein.

Fleming, L. N., Moore, I. N., Williams, D. G., Bliss, L. B., & Smith, K. C. (2013, June). *Social support: How Hispanic and Black engineering students perceive the support of peers, family, and faculty.* Presentation at the American Society for Engineering Education Annual Conference and Exposition Conference, Atlanta, GA.

Hegewisch, A., & Hartmann, H. (2014). *Occupational segregation and the gender wage gap: A job half done.* Washington, DC: The Institute for Women's Policy Research.

Jordan, D. (2006). *Sisters in science: Conversations with Black women scientists on race, gender, and their passion for science.* West Lafayette, IN: Purdue University Press.

Karet, G. (1999). Getting ahead in a man's world. *R& D Magazine, 41*(10), 10SE–11SE.

Kimbro, D. (2006). Defining success. *Black Collegian Online.* Retrieved from www.black-collegian.com/african/success.shtml

Landivar, L. C. (2013). *Disparities in STEM employment by sex, race, and Hispanic origin* (American Community Survey Reports ACS-24). Washington, DC: U.S. Census Bureau.

Leedy, P., & Ormrod, J. (2001). *Practical research: Planning and design.* Upper Saddle River, NJ: Prentice-Hall.

Lent, R. W., Brown, S. D., & Hackett, G. (1994). Toward a unifying social cognitive theory of career and academic interest, choice, and performance. *Journal of Vocational Behavior, 45*(1), 79–122.

Long, J. S. (2001). *From scarcity to visibility: Gender differences in the careers of doctoral scientists and engineers.* Washington, DC: National Academy Press.

Mabokela, R. O., & Green, A. L. (2001). *Sisters of the academy: Emergent Black women scholars in higher education.* Sterling, VA: Stylus.

MacLachlan, A. (2000, February). *The lives and careers of minority women scientists.* Presented at the National Association of Women in Education (NAWE) Conference, New Orleans, LA.

Malcolm, S. M., Chubin, D. E., & Jesse, J. K. (2004). *Standing our ground: A guidebook for STEM educators in the post-Michigan era.* Washington, DC: AAAS.

Martin, S. (1999). Gender, technology and work: Understanding patterns in women's employment in science and technology occupations. In *Proceedings: 1999 International Symposium on Technology and Society: Women and Technology: Historical, Societal, and Professional Perspectives* (pp. 118–129). New Brunswick, NJ: IEEE.

Moskal, B. M. (2000, October). *Looking to the future: Women in science and engineering.* Paper presentation at the Frontiers in Education Conference, Kansas City, MO.

Oakes, W., Mccomb, S., Mulkay, E., Berger, E., Blevins, L., Stamber, K., & Jones, J. (1999). Equipping undergraduates for the graduate school process. *Journal of Engineering Education, 88*(3), 353–359.

Ong, M., Wright, C., Espinosa, L. L., & Orfield, G. (2011). Inside the double bind: A synthesis of empirical research on undergraduate and graduate women of color in science, technology, engineering, and mathematics. *Harvard Education Review, 81*(2), 172–208.

Perna, L., Lundy-Wagner, V., Drezner, N. D., Gasman, M., Yoon, S., Bose, E., & Gary, S. (2009). The contribution of HBCUs to the preparation of Black women for STEM careers: A case study. *Research in Higher Education, 50*(1), 1–23.

Powell, A., Bagilhole, B., & Dainty, A. (2009). How women engineers do and undo gender: Consequences for gender equality. *Gender, Work & Organization, 16*(4), 411–428.

Prince, Z., (2013). *Study: Black women falling behind in STEM fields.* Washington, DC: Institute for Women's Policy Research.

Rhoton, L. A. (2011) Distancing as a gendered barrier: Understanding women scientists' gender practices. *Gender & Society, 25*(6), 696–716.

Sax, L. (1996, October). *The impact of college on post-college commitment to science careers: Gender differences in a nine-year follow-up of college freshmen.* Paper presented at the Annual Meeting of the Association for the Study of Higher Education, Memphis, TN.

Slaughter, J., & McPhail, I. (2007). New demands in engineering, science, and technology. *The Black Collegian,* First Semester 2007. Retrieved from the Black Collegian website, http://www.blackcollegian.com/new-demands-in-engineering-science-and-technology/

Springer, K. (2005). *Living for the revolution: Black feminist organizations, 1968–1980.* Durham, NC: Duke University Press.

Takahira, S., Goodings, D., & Byrnes, J. (1998). Retention and performance of male and female engineering students: An examination of academic and environmental variables. *Journal of Engineering Education, 87*(3), 297–304.

Turk-Bicakci, L., & Berger, A. (2014). *Leaving STEM: STEM Ph.D holders in non-STEM careers.* Washington, DC: American Institutes for Research.

The Mendoza Commission. (2000). *Land of plenty: Diversity as America's competitive edge in science, engineering and technology.* Washington, DC: Author.

United States Census Bureau. (2012). *U.S. census bureau projections show a slower growing, older, more diverse nation a half century from now* (press release). National Population Projections: 2012 to 2060. Retrieved from United States Census Bureau Newsroom Archives web site, http://www.census.gov/newsroom/releases/archives/population/cb12-243.html

Warren, W. (1999). *Black women scientists in the United States.* Bloomington: Indiana University Press.

Washington, B. T. (1901). *Up from slavery: An autobiography.* Garden City, NY: Doubleday.

Wulf, W. A. (1999). Diversity in engineering. In S. L. Blaisdell (Ed.), *Conference proceedings: Moving beyond individual programs to systemic change* (pp. 9–16). West Lafayette, IN: Women in Engineering Programs and Advocates Network Member Services.

Xu, Y. J. (2013) Career outcomes of STEM and non-STEM college graduates: Persistence in majored-field and influential factors in career choices. *Research in Higher Education, 54*(3), 349–382.

Yoder, B. L. (2011). Engineering by the numbers. In American Society for Engineering Education (Ed.), *Profiles of engineering and engineering technology colleges* (pp. 11–47). Washington, DC: ASEE.

Zurk, L. M., Simons, B., Parsons, R., & Cohen, D. (1995). When an advantage is not an advantage. *Communications of the ACM, 38*(12), 17–18.

CHAPTER 6

"WE SHOULD ALL HELP EACH OTHER"

Latina Undergraduates Overcoming Barriers in Computing

Heather Thiry
Sarah Hug

Pathways in STEM fields are especially difficult for women and girls of color who face multiple systems of oppression in science environments (Carlone & Johnson, 2007; Ong, Wright, Espinosa, & Orfield, 2011). The underrepresentation of Latinas in postsecondary computing in the United States is a particularly grave concern. Hispanics comprise only 13% of undergraduate degree recipients in all fields, far below the proportion of Hispanic youth in the general population (U.S. Census, 2011). Only 7% of baccalaureates in computer science in 2013 were granted to Hispanic U.S. citizens (National Center for Education Statistics (NCES), 2013). Less than 1% of computer science baccalaureates were awarded to Latinas. Even worse, in 2013, only two out of 863 CS PhD degrees were awarded to Latinas (NCES, 2013). And yet Hispanics are the fastest growing demographic group in the United

Women of Color In STEM, pages 91–109

States, comprising 16% of the total U.S. population, and nearly one quarter of the youth population (U.S. Census, 2011).

In this study, we focused on the experiences of Latinas within the field of computing and explored the ways in which Latina undergraduates come to see themselves, and to be seen by others, as successful and empowered computer science students. The larger purpose of the study was to understand how Latinas negotiated disciplinary cultures that subordinated them as women and as individuals of Hispanic origin. Through interviews with Latina computing majors, we explored the constraints and affordances they encountered in authoring competent identities in technical fields.

The research questions that drove this study were

1. How do Latinas negotiate the figured world of academic computing, particularly in regard to their computing expertise?
2. What social and cultural practices support Latinas in taking up professional identities in computing?
3. How does the intersectionality of race, class, and gender influence the position of Latinas in the figured world of academic computing and the identities that they produce within the discipline?

SOCIAL AND CULTURAL BARRIERS IN STEM DISCIPLINES FACED BY LATINAS

Women of color encounter numerous obstacles in pursuing STEM education and careers, especially the "double bind" of experiencing racism and sexism in traditionally White, male dominated STEM disciplines (Ong, Wright, Espinosa, & Orfield, 2011). While there is a burgeoning field of inquiry into the experiences of women of color in STEM, very little is known about the experiences of underrepresented minority women in computing fields. A thorough review of research studies of women of color in STEM revealed only 19 studies about women of color in computer science published in the last 40 years (Ong, 2011). These studies point to the legacy of the digital divide in which minority and low-income students lack access to technology, the social challenges for Latinas in computing, and the often nontraditional pathways pursued by Latinas in computing (Ong, 2011). Additionally, women of color may find that the science identities that they attempt to author in formal science spaces (e.g, degree programs, research labs, etc.) are either in conflict with their identities as women of color or are limited by the biases of others in their efforts to be recognized as legitimate scientists (Johnson, Brown, Carlone, & Cuevas, 2011).

In addition to challenges within STEM fields, Latinos/as face a number of sociocultural, economic, and educational obstacles in higher education degree attainment in general (Hurtado, Carter, & Spuler, 1996; Oseguera, Locks, & Vega, 2009). Lack of faculty support, discomfort on the university campus, and financial struggles contribute to high attrition rates of Latinos/as from higher education institutions (Gloria, Castellanos, Lopez, & Rosales, 2005; Santiago & Treindl, 2009). In STEM disciplines, cultural incongruence between minority communities and academic departments has been argued to contribute to the underrepresentation of Latinos/as, African-Americans, and Native Americans in these majors (Bonous-Hammarth, 2000; Cole & Espinoza 2008). Latino/a students are less likely than students from dominant communities to have completed college-ready coursework upon high school graduation (Tyson, Lee, Borman, & Hanson, 2007). Additionally, K–12 schools with sizable numbers of students from nondominant communities emphasize basic skills over higher-order thinking (Sleeter, 2005), which is detrimental to their success in advanced computing education (Margolis, 2008).

Latinos/as face multiple constraints within computing fields specifically. Racial and ethnic disparities in computing education can be attributed to the stubborn persistence of the digital divide, which is evident not only in access to devices and the internet but also in lack of technological knowledge and rich technical experience (Margolis, 2008; Warschauer, Knobel, & Stone, 2004). Low-income and rural high schools often offer little to no computing curriculum and high school teachers seldom influence female students of color towards computing (Varma, 2009). Hispanic women also face difficult transitions to college because of a lack of available family social capital and a delayed recognition of and access to institutional resources that may provide sources of social capital (Martin, Simmons, & Yu, 2013).

Perhaps, because of the challenges documented in Latinos' higher education and STEM experiences, minority-serving institutions have been shown to be an important STEM pathway for minority scientists. For example, hispanic-serving institutions (HSIs), meaning institutions that serve student populations that are at least 25% Hispanic, have been argued to play a pivotal role in increasing the number of Latino/a STEM degree holders because they enroll a large proportion of the nation's Latino/a students. Indeed, HSIs graduate nearly half of the Latino/a baccalaureates in the United States (Dowd, Malcolm, & Macias, 2010). Nevertheless, both male and female students in computer science (CS) departments at minority-serving institutions struggle with heavy workloads, poor teaching, lack of communication from faculty, and poor academic advising, and females report greater challenges in these areas than males (Varma & Hahn, 2007). On the other hand, women at minority-serving institutions may be better able to tolerate the geek, hacker culture associated with computing as the potential for high-status, lucrative jobs may outweigh the geek stigma for many minority women (Varma, 2007).

Despite the challenges faced by Latinas navigating higher education and computing fields, recent research has documented strategies that contribute to the increased persistence of women and underrepresented minority groups in STEM, including computing. The importance of effective mentoring in scientific and technical education cannot be overemphasized (Margolis & Fisher, 2002). Deliberate mentoring augments students' social and cultural capital, particularly for students whose familial backgrounds do not include college, studying science, and/or graduate school aspirations (Ovink &Veasey, 2011). Academic-focused extracurricular opportunities, such as undergraduate research, also contribute to the persistence of underrepresented minority students in STEM (Espinosa, 2011; Jones, Barlow, & Villarejo, 2010). STEM-based student organizations and campus resources that create support systems in STEM also contribute to the persistence of undergraduate women of color in STEM (Espinosa, 2011). Peer support networks, in particular, are vital for female undergraduates of color in STEM fields as they often experience a feeling of difference and a sense of not belonging in STEM departments (Tate & Linn, 2005).

Thus, researchers on STEM education have illuminated social, cultural, and economic reasons for the scarcity of women and minorities in computing and other STEM fields. Recent studies have identified strategies for supporting underrepresented minority and female students once they have enrolled in STEM majors. Yet researchers have not often focused on the ways in which specific underserved populations in STEM, such as Latinas in computing, experience intersectionality, negotiate barriers, and develop identities in fields in which they are overwhelmingly underrepresented. In this chapter, we identify the specific life history experiences that are associated with the development of empowered identities for Latinas in computing fields.

CONCEPTUAL FRAMEWORK

We used Holland, Lachicotte, Skinner, and Cain's (1998) concepts of identity and figured worlds to explore the experiences of Latinas within computing majors. Figured worlds are socially and historically situated realms of human activity with their own sets of values, norms, and expectations. Figured worlds may be far-reaching, such as academia, or local, such as a campus department. People enter into or are recruited into figured worlds and they "come to identify themselves as actors of more or less influence, more or less privilege, and more or less power in these worlds" (Holland et al., 1998, p. 60).

Identity is a valuable construct for interpreting the experiences of actors with less privilege and power within dominant cultural contexts, such as Latinas in computing. According to Holland et al. (1998), people may challenge taken-for granted notions and cultural constraints through the process of identity development. For example, Latinas may accept traditional, masculine notions of a computer scientist as a white or Asian male "hacker" and downplay the ways in which they differ from this stereotypical image or they may negotiate new definitions of computer scientist as community activist. Identities, including ways of becoming a computer scientist, are not static and fixed, nor do they spring from some "essential" characteristic such as gender or race. Rather, identities are works in progress and are formed in and through everyday practices, relationships, and interactions.

Identity involves not only actively identifying oneself as an actor within a specific social and cultural field, but also being seen by others as such. While this notion of identity allows for agency within peoples' lives, individuals are not free to adopt any identity they want. Indeed, they are constrained by given social and historical conditions; but, they may also improvise and act creatively within those conditions. The concept of identity within figured worlds allows us to examine hierarchy, status, and power within specific cultural realms of activity, such as academic departments or disciplines. This lens provides a framework for exploring the intersection of agency and structure and the ways in which individuals negotiate power within cultural domains. In this study, we use the concepts of identity and figured worlds to explore how Latinas navigate oftentimes difficult academic pathways and craft identities that counter the prevailing culture in computer science by valuing the intersectionality (Crenshaw, 1991) of being Latina in the figured world of computing.

RESEARCH DESIGN AND DATA SOURCES

We conducted semi-structured interviews to investigate—from the perspective of Latina actors in the figured world of computing—the interactions, practices, and relationships that facilitated or hindered their identification with and persistence in the discipline. All of our study participants were involved in the Computing Alliance of Hispanic-Serving Institutions (CAHSI), a National Science Foundation-sponsored consortium of 10 Hispanic-serving institutions (HSIs). CAHSI implements a number of pedagogical and programmatic innovations that support the recruitment, retention, and advancement of Hispanics in computing. Participating institutions span the cultural and regional diversity of Latinos/as in the United States, from a university in Puerto Rico, to ethnically diverse urban institutions in California, to universities in Florida with significant numbers of Cuban, Central, and South American students, to border universities in Texas and New Mexico with large populations of Mexican-American students. CAHSI serves as a national hub for Hispanic computing students, faculty, and professionals to support and network with one another. Due to the dire underrepresentation of Latina undergraduates in computing fields, CAHSI was an ideal site through which to identify research participants.

We conducted focus group interviews with all of the female student participants ($n = 22$) from CAHSI institutions at an academic conference that serves underrepresented minority students and faculty across a range of STEM disciplines. We sought to interview all Latina computing participants at this professional meeting to not only explore Latinas' experiences as computing students, but also to investigate how their participation in the professional conference may have influenced their identification with and commitment to the discipline. We scheduled focus groups with 22 women from seven institutions who attended the conference. Participants met with female peers from their institution when applicable, in groups from one to six total participants. Two interviewers conducted the focus groups, with one researcher chosen beforehand to lead the discussion. Of the 22 female focus group participants, almost all were undergraduate students (81%) and self-identified as Hispanic (77%). The rest of the participants were master's or doctoral students (19%) and identified as White (14%) or Asian (9%). Almost all participants were enrolled in computer science (CS) or computer engineering (CE) majors, although two students were enrolled in computer information systems (CIS), and one was a mathematics major with an emphasis in computer science. Interviews lasted 45 to 90 minutes, were digitally recorded, and transcribed verbatim. Interviews focused on participants' experiences within their departments and the larger field of computing. Sample interview questions include: "How did you first become interested in computer science?"; "Where do you 'fit' in your department?"; "Do you see any barriers that impact you as a Hispanic woman in computing?"; and "What has supported you in your pursuit of a computing degree?" Pseudonyms have been used to protect the confidentiality of participants.

ANALYSIS METHODS

Interview transcripts were coded using domain analysis (Spradley, 1980). Researchers searched for units of meaning within the data, coding interview transcripts for examples of "cover terms" within broader "domains." Taxonomies were then constructed linking coded examples to domain categories through a semantic relationship such as "is a kind of" or "is a way of doing." Domains were generated both deductively, based on concepts from our research questions and conceptual framework, and inductively, based on emergent themes from the data. For example, some deductive domain categories from our analysis include *barriers in computing, supports in computing*, and *professional identity*. Some inductive domain categories include:

gendered expectations and *family influence*. Two researchers generated the initial codebook in NVivo qualitative software. The researchers initially coded transcripts in tandem to identify emerging domains and to gauge inter-rater reliability. The researchers then divided the rest of the interviews and coded them separately, eventually merging them into one NVivo project. Throughout the coding process, the researchers met regularly to discuss emerging findings and to refine the codebook.

RESULTS

Barriers: Isolation and a Feeling of Difference

Because the women all attended minority-serving institutions, gender was often a more salient factor than race/ethnicity or social class in their everyday experiences in their computing departments. Women in all of the focus group interviews noted the challenges they faced as the only woman in a CS course, or as one of a few women. Many of them described the isolation they felt in their courses and their departments, and these challenges were typically gendered experiences. Women discussed the difficulty of dealing with competitive male peers or feeling that they could not turn to their male peers for help or support in a challenging course. A woman described the gendered differences between the mathematics and computer science departments, noting that she prefers the math department because there is a critical mass of women in the major. She also suggests that she perceives gender differences as static or fixed, as indicated by her comment that "boys" are competitive "by nature."

> In any given computer science class in school, there's probably a maximum of two or three girls in every 20 people. We are really outnumbered. I tend to stick along with the math majors because at my school there seems to be a more level playing field with math than computer science, but you have to prove yourself a little bit harder against the boys, because they tend to be so competitive, by nature.

Women also commented that they had to work harder and excel more than the men to be accepted by male students, or even professors, in their courses.

> It's hard because sometimes you're the only girl in the classroom and you feel kind of pressured because you have to demonstrate that you can be there, and that you're good enough to be there. So it can be hard. And if you have some professor that doesn't believe that you're good enough it's, like, kind of frustrating; it's hard.

Gender was not the only category that created a sense of "otherness" in our study. The contexts of Hispanic-serving institutions vary widely, from nearly 100% Hispanic students enrolled to 25%, and in some cases the share of Hispanic students in the computing departments did not mirror the enrollment at the institution, leading to even greater disparity. One graduate student who participated in a focus group noted that she felt "otherness" relating to ethnic identity, gender, and nationality.

> I come from a university where I'm almost the only girl in all my classes, and I'm particularly the only Hispanic girl, sometimes even the only American.

Her experience highlights the discrepancy between the U.S. workforce's need for computing professionals and computing departments' abilities to recruit and retain homegrown talent. For some students, the makeup of the student body can create a new sense of otherness based on nationality, even in one's own country of origin.

Barriers: Classroom Climate

The combination of isolation and oftentimes competitive male peers contributed to negative classroom climates in some courses. Participants in about half of the focus group interviews shared classroom experiences that they felt were negative due to their gender. Lara attributed her decision to switch out of the CS major to the isolation and poor climate she experienced in some of her courses.

> I started out as a CS major, and then I think about in between my second and third year, I switched to CIS [Computer Information Systems]. I really like programming, but it really is a hard degree. I also felt like in my classes, it was just very uncomfortable for me. I didn't enjoy being in class...like you don't feel welcome, you're not comfortable. If you're not comfortable, you're not learning, in my opinion. But you shouldn't feel so uncomfortable that you can't learn. Who do you turn to if you're a girl and you don't feel comfortable because there is only one other girl, and she doesn't talk either because she feels like there's only one other girl, and so who do you turn to for support?

Many of the women interpreted their interactions with men in courses through a gendered lens. They questioned whether gender influenced their male peers' or faculty's perceptions of them, as evidenced in the following comment about a negative interaction with a male peer over a homework assignment.

> I worry about the remarks that guys make. There was a project that I turned in, my friend, his R code was similar, like our logic, kind of followed the same

path. I got a higher grade than he did, and he kind of threw a fit, and it was kind of well, how much of this is because you are a girl. It's something that I worry about as far as academia.

Thus, women's negative interactions with male peers and faculty were related to the perceptions of some men that women are less capable and competent. These gendered interactions contributed to a poor climate in some, but not all, computing courses.

Barriers: Lack of Role Models

Due to their isolation in their departments, some of the focus group interviewees discussed a lack of role models in computing. The lack of role models was especially pronounced for students who had not had the opportunity to go to conferences designed to broaden participation in computing, such as a computing conference for Hispanics/Latinos/as, or a conference focused on women in computing. For example, Maria switched out of her CS department into computer information systems (CIS) and attributed the decision, in part, to the lack of role models and people like her in the computer science department.

> Again, I don't really have a ... I wouldn't say I had a direct role model as far as my CS track went. Maybe it would have made all the difference. Maybe I would have stayed in CS.

While many of the women had exposure to mentors and role models because of their involvement with CAHSI programming, a lack of role models could be devastating to women's educational and career goals.

Isolation often contributed to students' perceptions that they lacked supportive women to turn to for help. Many of the women noted that they felt uncomfortable being one of the few women in a class or in the department. Additionally, women felt uncomfortable asking the men for help or admitting that they did not know something for fear of being perceived as less capable than the men. In the following exchange, women discuss the reasons that some women do not complete the computer science degree. A lack of encouragement and support in male-dominated department also discourages women from completing their degrees.

> **Natalia:** Like, of 100 students who start in the computer engineering department, 15 are girls, from that 15, just 5 finish.
> **Estela:** And maybe it's not all that they don't like it, they feel like the men, the boys there and the professors there, some of them make your semester a headache because you're a girl.

> **Rosa:** I think some younger girls, when they take their first programming class, they get really frustrated because they've never been exposed to programming before. So they don't have anyone to tell them, "Hey, it's hard, it's difficult. I've been through that. So, just keep going." I actually met one yesterday who told me that she's taking her first programming class and she's hating it because she doesn't understand it, she doesn't have anyone to ask questions to or help her. I think it's just not having somebody else to talk to, because it's difficult for girls to approach a guy and say, "Hey, I need help. You know, I don't understand." It's difficult for me, mostly because we're girls and we don't want to feel like we don't know something. I don't know, it's different for us.

Evident in the quote above is the notion that the speaker identifies her status as a woman and her need to represent her gender well—to appear intelligent particularly when she is one of few representatives of her gender in an academic setting in which women are perceived to be lacking skill, experience, and/or talent.

Barriers: Experiencing Microaggressions

As Latinas in computing, the undergraduates described experiences of oppression in their discipline, in which they encountered hostility and racial and gender bias. They discussed isolation, marginalization, and microaggressions, meaning "brief and commonplace daily verbal, behavioral, or environmental indignities" that highlight difference and power between actors (Sue et al., 2007 p. 271). The women in this study encountered these slights in both local and global figured worlds of computing and often narrated their experiences with a focus on gender. For instance, Elisa recounted an experience at a conference where she felt ignored and invisible to a male professor, in stark contrast to the attention he gave to her male peers. This microaggression highlighted her subordinate status as a woman in the realm of computing.

> When we come to other conferences or other universities, I sometimes feel like, "I'm a woman." I've run into people, like other professors at other universities, and they don't pay attention to things I have to say. I just had that experience yesterday, actually. I was really bummed out. I had to introduce myself to a PhD professor, and I was explaining, "This is what I'm interested in." He went on to the next student, went to the next student, and then he comes back to me and he was like, "Did you already introduce yourself? Did you already tell me about yourself?" He gave everybody information about

scholarships, and I was like, "I'm the only one without a paper." I don't know if it was because I was female or what. Just little things . . . it's not very nice.

The women also became aware of their subordinated status as women in computing through difficult interactions with male peers within the competitive landscape of undergraduate computing classes, as described in the exchange below. Some male peers accepted them as computer scientists, while others held lower expectations or were dismissive of them. These interactions highlighted the devalued status of women within computing.

> **Josefina:** One thing that I notice, in any of my CS classes, there's a few guys that treat us maybe as equals. There's like five guys that are like, "Yes, they can do what we can do." But then the other ones, it seems like you have to do better. You have to study harder and you have to get better, or the same grades to be considered like, "Oh, maybe they can do it." Then sometimes it's like, still not, they're still just a girl.
> **Terese:** Most of the time I do better than all of them . . . But at the same time, it's this disconnect. It's this competitiveness where they don't want anybody being better than them, especially females. But it shouldn't be like that. We should all help each other.

In the exchange, Josefina and Terese lament the lack of support from male peers and contrast the value that they place on community with the competitive identities of many of their male peers. In turn, they propose new ways of becoming a computer scientist within academic spaces by "helping each other."

In these cases, and many others recounted by our focus group participants, gender—rather than ethnicity, class or other socially constructed categories—became the salient aspect of their identity through which they initially experienced power relationships in computing. Their focus on gender subordination may result from their attendance at Hispanic-serving institutions (HSI) in which Hispanics comprise at least 25% of the student population. Additionally, they participated in CAHSI, an organization dedicated to creating a community of Hispanic computing students, faculty, and professionals.

Becoming Successful Computer Scientists

Through the formal support provided by CAHSI and informal support fostered within peer networks, some women experienced shifts in identity similar to the Chicano activists/educators described by Urrieta (2007),

who took up an activist identity with a desire to educate others and give
back to their community. However, the life experiences that fostered these
shifts among our study participants were different from those in Urrieta's
research, with the exception of experiences of oppression. Similar to the
activists in Urrieta's study, experiences of oppression served as the spark
to ignite change in our study participants. The differences between the
Latina computer scientists and Urrieta's Chicano activists may arise from
differences in the sites of identity production, in the first case, community
activism, and in our study, an academic discipline.

Identity shifts that expanded women's notions of what it means to "be"
a computer scientist, and "who" can be a computer scientist, were often
fostered by interactions with role models. Interactions with role models also
led the students to a greater understanding of the intersectionality of their
identity within the landscape of computing, and the complex way in which
class, race, gender, and language may all play a role in subordination. For
instance, Julia commented on how hearing role models' stories at conferences helped her to situate herself within the field and envision that it is
possible to be a successful Latina computing professional.

> **Julia:** I think the conference is really good about exposing young
> females to PhDs that are also females, and have prominent
> positions in the universities. I think that's really exciting. It's
> nice to see people that are like me, who have similar back-
> grounds, who have succeeded. It's very inspiring, because
> you go through all these troubles, and you're starting out
> with your family, and not having too much money and all
> that stuff. You hear their stories, and they sound the same.
> I came from that background. Seeing people who have ac-
> complished that, and who have gotten a PhD, it's very inspir-
> ing, to a lot of girls.
>
> **Emma:** It's really exciting. Sometimes you just need to see that it's
> possible.
>
> **Benita:** It gives you hope.

Latina role models helped the women to frame their experiences of oppression in terms of the intersectionality of race, class, gender, nationality, and
language. Role models also offered students the knowledge and motivation
to navigate oppressive systems within the figured world of computing.

Some of the students also credited the systemic support they received
from CAHSI—which facilitated their involvement in disciplinary research,
travel to conferences, and interactions with Latina role models—with
their consciousness of underrepresentation. Often the role models were

not women they had access to in their institutional setting, as the share of Latina computing professors is alarmingly slight, but instead through the CAHSI network of multiple institutions, organizations, and corporate partners. Dolores commented that access to the tools and practices of her discipline in her research experience had helped her successfully navigate the academic pathway. Her research mentor also raised her awareness of the underrepresentation of Latinas in computing.

> I love my degree, and I'm really glad that CAHSI is helping our communities because we were talking about it in the research lab a few days ago, that not only the fact that there's no women [in computing] but no Hispanics, and [my mentor] was talking about how underrepresented we are. I'm glad that CAHSI is actually helping, because it feels encouraging that we actually can get somewhere, right? Because with no help, I mean, nobody would get anywhere. I'm really thankful for the opportunity.

Thus, many of the Latina undergraduates became critically aware of social and cultural inequities within the figured world of computing. Some women attributed their persistence in the major to this process of identity production, where they became critically conscious of power within the realm of computing, yet also gained confidence that they could successfully navigate—and possibly subvert—those power relationships. Participants gained this confidence through the combination of successful performance in the field and recognition of that success, similar to the women of color in Carlone and Johnson's (2007) study of science identity development.

As the Latinas in our study displayed competence and mastery in their disciplinary knowledge through research experiences and conferences, not only did they come to see themselves differently, others began to view them differently as well. Rosa described a shift in the way that her male peers perceived the Latinas in her department. The student's engagement in professional activities had conferred status to them within the local figured world of their department and others began to see them as successful computer science students.

> Some of (our male peers), they don't know us, and I guess they don't know what we're doing and, I guess they judge us. Or they have this stereotype of the girls who are not good enough...they treat me with respect now, *"Oh, wow, you're going to conferences, that's really cool. Wow, I've never done that before. You must be really smart, you work really hard."*

In this way, many participants gained status within their departments, seeing themselves, and being seen, as successful computer scientists.

Producing Empowered Identities

At four institutions, these shifts in identity sparked a more empowered stance among participants. As already noted, the women often felt isolated, disenfranchised, and disrespected by some of their male peers and in some interactions outside of their departments. As a result of their critical awareness of the intersectionality of gender, race, class, and language within the figured world of computing, they began to subvert these power relationships by creating academically oriented clubs and other supportive peer networks. Terese, one of the founders of a computing club on her campus, described its goals of creating a stronger sense of community in the department, not just for women, but for all students.

> Basically, the goal is to create this sense of community within the department for students to feel comfortable. We have study sessions before the meetings, so students can just come, sit together with other students, and do their homework together. It's great because within that mix there is some lower classmen and upper classmen, and so there's always help there, because everybody is friendly.

Terese reflected on her reasons for attending a conference dedicated to the advancement of underrepresented populations in scientific fields. Her motivations reflect her burgeoning understanding of the complex intersectionality of gender and ethnicity within computing. She hoped to take her new understanding of the positionality of Latinas in computing to encourage underrepresented minority girls in her local area to enter into and persist in STEM fields. Though she embraced some aspects of the traditional culture of computing, and had a professional goal of working at Google as a programmer, Terese had begun to incorporate outreach, mentoring, and local activism into her computer science identity.

> What I can take back [from the conference] is getting girls and minorities [into computing]. Where we work is a HSI, Hispanic-serving institution, primarily, so since not only are women underrepresented but also minorities, what we can take from this conference is to help the students and the girls and the kids in our area. That's what I'm hoping to get out of the conference is new ideas, because it's so hard to keep using the same old ones. When you feel like they're only helping so much.

On another campus, the women negotiated a new organizational identity for their campus computer science club. Aida described how the former student president of the club was a little iffy, and he was only wanting to do game stuff. He was like, "We're going to have some LAN parties, and just get together and game all day." That was all he was about. I was like, "Yes, that would be fun to do, but we need to do other stuff."

A group of undergraduate women, mostly Latina, assumed the leadership of the club and created a space where outreach, community service, and professional development were valued. They shifted the values of the club away from an individualistic focus on technical proficiency to a focus on community.

Last year, and this year, we have a woman president and vice president. Last year, Ana was president and I was vice president. This time around, I'm president and Sofia is vice president. We're showing a bigger appearance for women in the CS area, and wanting to do more things. But part of our club, part of our goal, is not just to help you tutor or program or something like that. We try and get all the CS people together outside of classes, and outside of school work, and socialize, get to know each other. It's been a great way to get to know people. Every year it seems like the officers seem to be getting better, and having the interests of the club members in mind. We got more involved with community service and did relay for life. Last year, we actually took charge of doing a trip for the computer science club. We were able to raise money throughout the year, and we went up to an advanced computing center.

At other institutions, students did not start formal extracurricular clubs, but developed informal peer networks for support. Academically inclined Latinas developed relationships with each other in the academic spaces of research groups, conferences, or classes. These networks provided personal support and encouragement. Leticia commented on an informal network of women in her computer science department.

We know that within our group, we are there for the same reasons. We need to just help each other and find support when somebody may need tutoring or something you are struggling in. Or just like a conversation, a cup of coffee, in those types of things I really find support.

In the local figured worlds of their academic departments, some women began to organize their subjectivities around the issue of underrepresentation in computing, and thus enacted identities that valued being a Latina in computing. As Holland et al. (1998) theorized, the social interactions in the localized and temporal spaces of the computing clubs and informal peer networks gave voice to the lived experiences of Latinas in computing. In this process, some women gained a deeper understanding of the cultural, political, and historical landscape of Latinas in computing, and produced identities that contested the privileging of White and Asian male "hacker" culture in computer science. Much like the role models that they accessed through conferences who helped to foster their own shifts in identity, some of the Latina undergraduates began to serve as "significant narrators" to younger students of local figured worlds in which they participated (Urrieta, 2007). As significant narrators, they encouraged the girls to enter into computing, while helping them to navigate the oftentimes treacherous pathways in the discipline. In this way, some of the Latinas in this study produced identities that recognized the intersectionality of race, gender, and class within computing, and redefined computer scientist as someone who values community, outreach, and mentoring over individualism and competition.

CONCLUSION

The Latinas in our study shared several common threads in their life history experiences that facilitated shifts in their identity within the professional and academic landscape of computing. The four life experiences related to professional empowerment were (a) experiencing discrimination and oppression, (b) gaining a critical understanding of oppression through interactions with role models from similar backgrounds, (c) engaging in successful disciplinary performances, and (d) teaching or mentoring others. The Latinas in our study recounted many instances of bias and microaggressions, yet participants' shift away from isolation and marginalization was fostered by interactions with Latina role models who situated the student's negative experiences within inequitable social, cultural, and historical legacies in computing. Participants began to see that their struggles were not isolated or unique. The role models served as catalysts to transform the student's understanding of their own experiences and helped to redefine their professional identities as Latinas in computing. Additionally, successful disciplinary performances in research and at conferences were pivotal in conferring status to the women within their departments and within the broader figured world of computing. These two experiences—interactions with role models and successful disciplinary performance—helped the women to see themselves, and to be seen by male peers and others, as competent computer scientists. Participants then enacted these professionally empowered identities by teaching and mentoring other young women in their own departments and in their local communities. These life history experiences represent identity shifts away from an individualistic, isolated experience of computing to one defined by reflection, community, and teaching.

The Latinas in this study challenged the taken-for-granted notion of computing as a competitive, individualistic enterprise predicated on technical proficiency dominated by White or Asian, male hackers. This study provides a glimpse into the way in which interactions and practices can foster, or impede, identification with the discipline for Latinas in computing. STEM faculty, professionals, and policymakers and others concerned with broadening participation in STEM should increase access to role models who can place students' position as women or girls of color within larger social and cultural systems of oppression. Educators must also provide plentiful opportunities for women and girls of color to engage deeply in the discipline and to be recognized for doing so. Additionally, students facing the "double bind" in STEM benefited from the opportunity to teach and mentor younger girls of color and, in turn, help them to navigate disciplinary terrain. Formal mentoring programs where women and girls of color have the opportunity to be mentored and yet also mentor others may help to counter many of the barriers faced within STEM disciplines.

While many of the negative experiences of the Latinas in our study have been documented in the STEM education research literature, the processes through which Latinas shift their CS identities and persist in computing disciplines has not been documented to date. Likewise, STEM education researchers have explored the positive effects of role models but have rarely investigated the ability of role models to illuminate social and cultural disparities and, thus, empower novices from nondominant communities. Yet, through interactions with role models and successful disciplinary performances, Latinas in this study redefined what it means to be a computer scientist and produced computer science identities that value community, outreach, and cooperation over individualism and competition.

REFERENCES

Bonous-Hammarth, M. (2000). Pathways to success: Affirming opportunities for science, mathematics, and engineering majors. *The Journal of Negro Education, 69*(1/2), 92–111.

Carlone, H., & Johnson, A. (2007). Understanding the science experiences of successful women of color: Science identity as an analytic lens. *Journal of Research in Science Teaching, 44*(8), 1187–1218.

Cole, D., & Espinoza, A. (2008). Examining the academic success of Latino students in science, technology, engineering and mathematics (STEM) majors. *Journal of College Student Development, 49*(4), 285–300.

Crenshaw, K. (1991). Mapping the margins: Intersectionality, identity politics, and violence against women of color. *Stanford Law Review, 43*(6), 1241–1299.

Dowd, A. C., Malcom, L. E., & Macias, E. E. (2010). *Improving transfer access to STEM bachelor's degrees at Hispanic Serving Institutions through the America COMPETES Act.* Los Angeles: University of Southern California.

Espinosa, L. L. (2011). Pipelines and pathways: Women of color in undergraduate STEM majors and the college experiences that contribute to persistence. *Harvard Educational Review, 81*(2), 209–240.

Gloria, A., Castellanos, J., Lopez, A.G., & Rosales, R. (2005). An examination of academic nonpersistence decisions of Latino undergraduates. *Hispanic Journal of Behavioral Sciences, 27*(2), 202–223.

Holland, D., Lachicotte, W., Jr., Skinner, D., & Cain, C. (1998). *Identity and agency in cultural worlds.* Cambridge, MA: Harvard University Press.

Hurtado, S., Carter, D. F., & Spuler, A. (1996). Latino student transition to college: Assessing difficulties and factors in successful college adjustment. *Research in Higher Education, 37*(2), 135–157.

Johnson, A., Brown, J., Carlone, H., & Cuevas, A .K. (2011). Authoring identity amidst the treacherous terrain of science: A multiracial feminist examination of the journeys of three women of color in science. *Journal of Research in Science Teaching, 48*(4), 339–366.

Jones, M. T., Barlow, A. E. L., & Villarejo, M. (2010). Importance of undergraduate research for minority persistence and achievement in biology. *The Journal of Higher Education, 81*(1), 82–115.

Margolis, J. (2008). *Stuck in the shallow end: Education, race, and computing.* Cambridge, MA: MIT Press.

Margolis, J., & Fisher, A. (2002). *Unlocking the clubhouse: Women in computing.* Cambridge, MA: MIT Press.

National Center for Education Statistics. (2013). *Digest of education statistics.* Washington, DC: National Center for Education Statistics, Institute of Education Sciences, U.S. Department of Education.

Martin, J. P., Simmons, D. R., & Yu, S. L. (2013). The role of social capital in the experiences of Hispanic women engineering majors. *Journal of Engineering Education, 102*(2), 227–243.

Ong, M. (2011). The status of women of color in computer science: Addressing the challenges of increasing the number of women of color in computing and ensuring their success. *Communications of the ACM, 54*(7), 32–34.

Ong, M., Wright, C., Espinosa, L. L., & Orfield, G. (2011). Inside the double bind: A synthesis of empirical research on undergraduate and graduate women of color in science, technology, engineering, and mathematics. *Harvard Educational Review, 81*(2), 172–208.

Oseguera,L., Locks, A., & Vega, I. (2009). Increasing Latina/o students' baccalaureate attainment: A focus on retention. *Journal of Hispanic Higher Education, 8*(1), 23–53.

Ovink, S. M., & Veazey, B. D. (2011). More than "getting us through": A case study in cultural capital enrichment of underrepresented minority undergraduates. *Research in Higher Education, 52,* 370–394.

Santiago, D., & Treindl, T. (2009) *Taking stock: Higher education and Latinos.* Washington, DC: Excelencia in Education.

Sleeter, C. (2005). *Un-standardizing curriculum: Multicultural teaching in the standards-based classroom.* New York, NY: Teachers College Press.

Spradley, J. P. (1980). *Participant observation.* New York, NY: Holt, Rinehart, and Winston.

Sue, D. W., Capodilupo, C. M., Torino, G. C., Bucceri, J. M., Holder, A., Nadal, K. L., & Esquilin, M. (2007). Racial microaggressions in everyday life: implications for clinical practice. *American Psychologist, 62*(4), 271–286.

Tate, E. D., & Linn, M. C. (2005). How does identity shape the experiences of women of color engineering students? *Journal of Science Education and Technology, 14*(5/6), 483–493.

Tyson, W., Lee, R., Borman, K., & Hanson, M. A. (2007). Science, technology, engineering, and mathematics (STEM) pathways: High school science and mathematics coursework and postsecondary degree attainment. *Journal of Education for Students Placed at Risk, 12*(3), 243–270.

United States Census. (2011). *Explore census data.* Retrieved from https://data.census .gov/cedsci

Urrieta, L., Jr. (2007). Identity production in figured worlds: How some Mexican Americans become Chicana/o activist educators. *Urban Review, 39*(2), 117–144.

Varma, R. (2007). Women in computing: The role of geek culture. *Science as Culture, 16*(4), 359–376.

Varma, R. (2009). Gender differences in factors influencing students towards computing. *Computer Science Education, 19*(1), 37–49.

Varma, R., & Hahn, H. (2007). Gender differences in students' experiences in computing education in the United States. *International Journal of Engineering Education, 23*(2), 361–367.

Warschauer, M., Knobel, M., & Stone, L. (2004). Technology and equity in schooling: Deconstructing the digital divide. *Educational Policy, 18*(4), 562–588.

CHAPTER 7

HOW AN AFRICAN AMERICAN FEMALE ACCOMPLISHES HER GOAL TO GET TO HIGHER EDUCATION

Solongo Chuluunbaatar

It has been well known that the minority groups of students in elementary to high school such as African Americans, Latinos, and Native Americans score lower than White students do on examinations of basic skills, problem-solving, problem applications, and college entrance (Secada, 1992; Tate, 1997). According to Johnson et al. (2011), Black, Latino, and American Indian students in the United States graduate from high school at lower rates (about 60%) than White and Asian students (81% and 90%, respectively) (p. 340).

The National Council of Teachers of Mathematics (NCTM, 1989, 2000) suggests that students need to improve their problem-solving and reasoning abilities and make connections in mathematics. The NCTM also recommends that teachers need to know how students' linguistic, ethnic, and racial backgrounds influence their learning. However, it is not suggested how

Women of Color In STEM, pages 111–124
Copyright © 2021 by Information Age Publishing
All rights of reproduction in any form reserved.

teachers achieve this knowledge of students (Gutierrez, 1999). The similar concern was addressed by Allexsaht-Snider and Hart (2001) that

> policymakers and researchers have acknowledged these achievement differences in their calls for improving mathematics learning for all students. What has not been clear is how teachers and administrators in individual schools and districts throughout the country might accomplish equity in mathematics with their students. (p. 1)

Thus, the mathematics performance gap between minority students and Whites is well recognized by researchers. In addition, it has been an ongoing goal for the teachers and scholars to search for ways to improve this issue. However, it is equally important to find out the reason why these minority groups of students are unable to succeed in their mathematics and science learning as other White students.

In partial answer to this question, Malloy and Malloy (1998) claimed,

> Public education of America's students has for over a century provided educational opportunities to students using cultural traditions and theories of learning based on the dominant or majority population...When students who generally were not of the dominant culture experienced difficulty functioning within parameters of the school, they were placed in lower academic classes, where they were labeled as deficient and devalued for their academic capabilities. (p. 246)

Students from the dominant culture were able to succeed in their mathematics learning because that was how the educational system was designed. Students who did not belong to the dominant culture were left behind and struggled to fit into the system. In order to help the minority group students to adopt this education system, during the past decade, reforms have been suggested such as NCTM statement about understanding students' backgrounds related to their learning. However, some researchers believe that "despite the NCTM acknowledgment of cultural differences, most mathematics teaching reforms have ignored the needs of minority children" (Brenner, 1998, p. 214).

New methods and programs for teaching mathematics were first tested on general populations and intended to extend to minority groups later. It is noted by several researchers that the performance gap between students of color and White children had grown smaller during the 1980s and 1990s (Secada, 1992; Tate, 1997). Brenner (1998), however, stated that new evidence again showing the significant difference between two groups and this achievement gap does not narrow because of most interventions, and White children often gain most from new programs.

Core curriculum and multicultural education are two main approaches advocated in the current school reform movement. Core curriculum demands higher standards and multicultural education focuses on cultural differences in content and form. Ogbu (1992) criticized that neither of these approaches adequately addresses the problem of those minority groups who have not traditionally done well in school. Instead, Ogbu declared that the crucial issue in cultural diversity and learning is the relationship between the minority cultures and the American dominant culture. In his research, he recognizes that some of the minority groups were doing very well in school in spite of their language and cultural differences, and some were not. He divides the minority groups into two categories: (a) voluntary minorities—immigrants who come to the United States with their own will, and (b) involuntary minorities—people who were originally brought into the United States or any other society against their will such as slavery, conquest, colonization, or forced labor.

Voluntary minorities are the people who voluntarily moved to America to seek a better future or opportunity because they desired more economic well being and political freedom. "They usually experience challenges related to learning because of their cultural and language differences. But they do not experience lingering, disproportionate school failure" (Ogbu, 1992, p. 8)

On the other hand, involuntary minorities experience greater and persistent difficulties with school learning because they were denied true assimilation into the dominant society. Ogbu (1992) gives specific examples of involuntary minorities as American Indian, African American, early Mexican Americans, and Native Hawaiians. He continues to verify that involuntary minorities consider the school system as a "white thing." Therefore, since they do not want to achieve what Whites expect (if they do then they would be considered as outside of their own community), they do poorly in school.

While race and culture play an important role in the achievement gap of minority students, gender is an equally vital issue that needs to be addressed in math and science learning. Johnson et al. (2011) stated, "Girls in every racial group graduate at higher rates than boys . . . in a study using a different definition of graduation, for instance, 59% of African American girls graduated in 2003 versus 48% of African American boys; this was contrasted with 79% of White girls and 74% of White boys" (p. 340). Although girls graduate at higher rates than boys, it is also a known fact that there are fewer women in science than men because minority women have less opportunity to get higher education in math and science fields.

Despite the obstacles they encounter, there are a number of women who successfully complete math and science degrees in college and graduate level. How does a minority woman describe her successful educational experiences in math and science as racialized and gendered forms of experience? This study portrays how one African American female accomplishes her goal to get higher education by focusing on the factors that she needed to overcome.

THEORETICAL FRAMEWORK

This study centered on the success story of an African American female student as she described her experiences and obstacles to study science. Her narratives fit into the four levels of guiding investigations of identity that Martin (2000) developed: (a) sociohistorical level, (b) community level, (c) school level, and (d) individual level. In addition to Martin's framework, race and gender are categorized as subgroups within these four main levels.

First, the sociohistorical level discusses differential treatment in mathematics-related contexts that prevented African Americans from succeeding. Second, the community level covers expectations of African American parents and motivations to learn mathematics and science. Third, the school level argues school standards and teacher's role in student's abilities and success. Fourth, the individual level focuses on personal identities, goals, and motivation to learn mathematics and science.

The initial theme was based on racial and gender issues of minority women in science; however, Martin's multilevel framework serves as the main category and race and gender are categorized as subgroups within these four main levels.

RESEARCH DESIGN

Key Informant

The goal of this study focuses on the mathematics and science experiences and narratives of an African American female as she discusses her success story being a Black female. The participant of this study, whom I call Michelle, is a current PhD at a larger university in Chicago. She is in her early 40s and holds a master's degree in education. She grew up and lived in Chicago for her whole life.

Michelle's background suited this study because her undergraduate degree was in chemistry, and she is a successful PhD student who is currently taking a statistics class as one of her degree requirement classes. She has expressed her concern and fear for taking statistics classes because it would involve mathematics. My initial goal to interview her was to find out the following: (a) how she decided to major in chemistry in her undergraduate degree despite of the obstacles many minority female students face, (b) what experiences she had as a female African American undergraduate

science student and how this influenced her to succeed in higher education, and (c) how her mathematics learning experience was and if that experience has caused the current fear of taking this statistics class.

As I discovered her undergraduate mathematics experience, I was hoping
to find out where the fear of taking statistics class (she assumes statistics involves mathematics) comes from. I was also interested in asking what caused
her to discontinue studying science (chemistry) and changing her career. Most
of all, I wanted to learn her success stories as she pursued higher education.

Michelle was a perfect participation for this study to understand identity
development because of her demographic background and academic experience in science. This study was concentrated on her experience as both
racialized and gendered. Although Michelle did not complete an advanced
degree in science or work in science-based professions, understanding her
pathways to higher education would make meaning of mathematics and
science experience that are related to the race and gender issue.

Procedure

I interviewed Michelle while we were having lunch together in a quiet
area and the interview was tape-recorded. The interview lasted an hour and
half and the interview was a semi-structured interview with open-ended
questions. I had a written interview protocol in the beginning; however, as
the interview went on, I did not ask the questions in the order that was initially planned. I had to ask new questions to clarify or to make the interview
flow more naturally. The interviewee was very open and pleasant. Michelle
was willing to share her experience honestly and took her time to think
when needed. At some point, Michelle became emotional (grateful for her
parents and husband) when she talked about her family. She commented
that many of the questions in this interview made her reflect deeper about
things that she did not think of previously.

There was a second interview (follow-up interview) 3 weeks after the first
interview in which the conditions and environment were very similar to the
first interview. The second interview was shorter (20 minutes), and it was
tape-recorded. The purpose of the second interview was to make sure the
assertions were correct. I also asked some additional questions that were relevant to the key themes. The selected parts of the interview were transcribed.

ANALYSIS

After the initial interview, I listened to the recorded interview and took a de-
tailed note. My goal was to find out themes related to the race and gender issue from Michelle's narrative. As I was listening to the interview, I highlighted

the important points and tried to organize them into subgroups. In addition to the second interview (the follow-up interview), I occasionally arranged informal discussions with Michelle to observe her opinions on the key theme. It became clear that Michelle's narrative would be best analyzed through Martin's (2000) multilevel framework. My initial theme was based on racial and gender issues of minority women in science; however, in addition to the race and gender issue, Michelle's story was connected to sociohistorical, community, school, and individual level (main category). Race and gender are categorized as subgroups within these four main groups.

Sociohistorical Level

Michelle believes that the south side of Chicago has always been segregated. When she became a university student, she knew what to expect (she would not find many African American peers there).

Community Level

Michelle talked about how education plays an important role in one's life and how her parents had high expectations from her and her siblings.

School Level

Michelle shared about her chemistry teacher and her influence on her decision about majoring in chemistry. Michelle knew it is important to attend in a school that has higher standards.

Individual Level

Michelle believes it is important to plan from an early age in order to be a successful student. Her personal story illustrates how she resisted the opportunity gap that is linked to race and gender.

FINDINGS

Michelle had always enjoyed learning mathematics and science and being one of the best students in her class. Her parents always taught their children to get the highest education possible because they believed education was the key to success and independence. Michelle did not focus on what people think of her; instead, she focused on things that she enjoyed doing. Her personal experience illustrates what she had to do to overcome the obstacles and achieve her goal in her life. There are four main categories, sociohistorical, community, school, and individual level, in which race and gender are the subcategories.

Sociohistorical Level

Racial Issue in Sociohistorical Level

One of my first questions was about Michelle's early education. When I asked Michelle how she would describe her elementary school's racial mix, she firmly replied that it was 99.99% a Black school and continued:

> That is the one thing about Chicago is, it is very segregated. It can be . . . certain areas of Chicago are very segregated . . . typically in the south side, African Americans go to school.

When Michelle decided to study at a college that was located in the north side of Chicago, she knew what to expect, that she would not find many African American peers there. As she pursued her master's and PhD degrees, she was not surprised that she had very few African American students in her classes. When I questioned why she thinks there are less African American students in higher education, she replied that

> I have never thought about that. I had always lived in my community until I attended college in the north side of the Chicago and it was clear that there would be a few African Americans . . . It is sad but most African Americans are struggling with education even though they know education is important.

Gender Issue in Sociohistorical Level

Michelle thinks some things have changed since she went to elementary school 20 years ago when I asked about gender issue in education. Specifically, she remembers that in her elementary and high school, boys equally succeeded as girls did. However, today it seems like it became a social norm that African American boys are not expected to succeed in school.

> **M:** I was a second top student in my class because a boy beat me out. Ratio of successful students was equal within girls and boys in early 80s when I went to school. But now African American males are struggling academically. Today if he is smart then it is almost like a surprise.

> **SC:** How do you know? Do you have experience on that?
> **M:** From my teaching experience. Today girls have motivation to achieve and get out of school and go to a college. But boys... they became playful.
> **SC:** Have you thought why? Why is it different from twenty years ago?
> **M:** Hmm. I do not know. There are many journals that researchers write about it. I do not know the reason why African American boys struggle academically. That is why I am here to study and find about it.

My initial goal was to find out how she felt being a female science major student at the university. When I asked Michelle how she felt being one of the few female students in her undergraduate science classes, she did not pay attention to the gender ratio. While she expected racial disproportion, she did not expect gender disproportion in her science career because she had never taken notice about it. She remembers that most of her undergraduate science classes consisted of 60% male and 40% female. She always thought there were more male students because female students either got married and had children or chose easier majors.

Community Level

Racial Issue in Community Level

Michelle's parents always told her that education plays an important role in one's life, and her parents had very high expectations from her and her siblings. She recalls that her motivation was to please her parents. Moreover, she knew that she should do well academically if she wanted to have opportunities. When I asked her about why Asian Americans do well in mathematics and science, she said:

> Education is great priority among Asian American community, much more than American culture. Especially, in my community (African American community), they know education is important, but there are so many struggles... parents struggled before hand so it is almost like a cycle.

As her parents stressed the importance of education, Michelle and her husband always motivated their four children to succeed academically. Michelle's husband graduated from high school and did not go to a college, which he regrets later. Michelle's husband is a mail carrier, and he thinks that he would have gotten a better job if he had a college degree. For that reason, he has always pushed his children to appreciate education.

Michelle also pointed out the importance of planning strategy in higher education. When I asked how she and her sisters were able to get higher education in spite of the fact that few African American students pursue higher education, she replied that her parents planned early. It is important to plan early if one wants to go to a college because if there is no plan then it is difficult to catch up in high school. Transcripts will show the grades and one has to have good grades in order to get into a college.

Gender Issue in Community Level

Michelle's mother was a schoolteacher, and she went back to school later to get her master's degree. Her mother's example motivated her to get higher education. In fact, both of her sisters also have master's degrees and enjoy going to school. Michelle's mother always taught her daughters that women need their freedom and education was the path to have that freedom. When Michelle was asked about if women have the same ability as men in science, she believes that it is not about ability rather it is about expectation. Generally, women compared to men are less likely to pursue a higher education degree. Michelle did not use her chemistry degree after her graduation from college because she got married and had children; yet, she went back to get her master's degree when her children became older because she wanted to follow her mother's footstep to pursue higher education.

School Level

Racial Issue in School Level: School Standards

Michelle continuously expressed her opinion about the importance of the school standards throughout the interview. Michelle's father sent her to a Catholic high school because he felt that it had higher standards. Michelle and her husband repeated that pattern when they made a decision about their children's school. Michelle stated that:

> Public schools are not decent as before. Twenty years ago when I went to public school, it was decent. The area we grew up was middle class neighborhood then, but now it is not middle class anymore, much poor now. We moved to south suburbs where our children would get better education. It has mostly African American children, but the school has better standards.

Racial Issue in School Level: Teacher Role

Besides the importance of school standards, Michelle shared about her chemistry teacher and her influence on her decision about majoring in chemistry. Her high school chemistry teacher was such a great teacher that her example made Michelle decide to become a chemistry teacher. Her teacher had beliefs about students' abilities and she motivated them to succeed in chemistry.

Racial Issue in School Level: Student's and Parents' Belief About Teachers

According to Michelle's narrative, one of the reasons why Asian Americans do well academically is closely related to the student's belief about teachers. The same principle applies to the reason why many African American students struggle academically. Michelle believes that Asian American culture teaches children to respect teachers more than African Americans do.

> Here, unless you are a professor at university, you are not well respected... But Asian American parents seldom think of teachers as they are wrong. If you do something wrong and teachers call parents... parents and teachers are like allies. When I was growing up, I knew I could not bring bad grade. It is different today. Today parents, especially African American parents... it is sad but it is true... may or may not believe in teachers... Parents are passing blame to someone else (teachers mostly) for children's education responsibilities.

Michelle feels if the people's perception of respecting teachers changes to a positive direction then students would give more respect to teachers and this would lead to success.

{H4}**Gender issue in school level.** As mentioned previously, Michelle's parents were very concerned about the standards of the school system; therefore, her father chose a Catholic high school, believing it is better than a public school. Michelle's father was very specific about choosing all girls school because he believed it is better for girls.

> **M:** That time I thought I was receiving the best education. I thought my high school was challenging; but, when I got to freshman class, I could see other people are better than me.
>
> **SC:** What do you mean by other people?
>
> **M:** That is the thing, you see, I was the only African American student in most of my classes in addition to being one of the few women.
>
> **SC:** As a female student and African American, did you think you were expected to achieve as well as other students?
>
> **M:** That is a very good question! I did not think about gender before. I always knew education was important, so I was expected to achieve. Catholic high schools did not have calculus class and I struggled in calculus. In fact, because I did not do well in calculus I could not get a BS degree which was required if I wanted to teach chemistry. There were more

males but there were enough girls that I made friends, that I did not feel alienated.

Individual Level: Racial Issue in Individual level

Michelle identified the student achievement role as one of the factors of her successful experience. When I asked how other students viewed her, she believed that her individual goal was more important than what others thought about her. From elementary to high school, some students teased her for being smart; however, she did not view that as a negative experience because she was in a high-achieving class. She was surrounded with friends and classmates who shared similar goals; therefore, being smart made her feel good about herself. Indeed, being smart influenced her to have a positive self-esteem. Outside of the school, Michelle was well-respected within her neighborhood and community because of her academic success in her classes including her mathematics and science class. Friends and family often asked her help, which made her feel good about herself. Moreover, helping and tutoring experience led her to choose a teaching career.

When she was asked about her racial experience in the undergraduate science classes, she replied:

> **M:** Often I was the only African American student in my classes and I felt alienated. I am also a shy person. But I made friends. I had many Filipino friends that I studied together. Oh, I also had some Indian friends too.
>
> **SC:** Were they international students? Did you have more friends that are international?
>
> **M:** Yes, I think so. I had more international friends.
>
> **SC:** Why?
>
> **M:** I do not know. Now that I think back, I did have more international friends.
>
> **SC:** You mentioned you felt alienated. Do you think there are factors that prevent or discourage African Americans from going into science?
>
> **M:** I think it has something to do with their educational struggle. They need higher grades to go to a college and it takes dedication to get good grades in school.

Michelle commented that despite her background, her focus was on education. She liked science and wanted to major in science; therefore, she did not consider what race was the majority of students. She always had friends who accepted her as who she was. That was her motivation to succeed in the science major.

Gender Issue in Individual Level

According to Michelle's personal experience, gender issues played fewer roles in her science education than race issues did. She did not consider gender issues in her educational success. However, she recalled her son's experience in high school. Her son was always the best student in his class, and he was teased for being smart. On the other hand, her daughter was not teased for being smart. Michelle explained:

> I do not know if it is gender issue, maybe it is because in African American community, girls are the ones who expected to be better. Boys are not expected to be better today. As I said before, it was not like that when I was growing up.

Despite that challenge, Michelle's son continued to be the best student, graduated from college, and earned a degree in finance. Once he saw he could do well in school, it was his motivation to get good grades and feel good about himself. He did not have to worry about getting teased because he managed to have a group of friends that was supportive. His parents did not have to push him to succeed either because academic achievement became natural to him and he continued to do well in school especially in his mathematics classes.

CONCLUSION

My preliminary purpose of this interview was to find out how one African American female student successfully pursued a science degree, despite the obstacles many minority female students encountered. I started my interview with her mathematics learning experience and because of her fear of taking statistics class as a graduate student. I discovered that she had a positive mathematics learning experience until she took calculus class in college. However, calculus experience did not cause her fear of taking statistics class. In fact, she enjoyed doing algebra part of the statistics class; it is the theoretical part of statistics that she was worried about.

My initial goal of this study was to find out racial and gender issues of minority women in science; however, in addition to the race and gender issue, Michelle's story was connected to sociohistorical, community, school, and individual level. Race and gender are categorized as subgroups within these four main groups.

Sociohistorical Level

Michelle had always been aware of Chicago being a segregated city, and she expected that there would be fewer African American students in higher education. Michelle noticed that when she went to school 20 years ago, boys equally succeeded as girls did. However, today it became a social norm that African American boys were not expected to succeed in school.

Community Level

Michelle always knew that education played an important role in one's life and her parents had high expectations from her and her siblings. Michelle and her husband also motivated their four children to succeed academically. Michelle also pointed out the importance of planning strategy in higher education. As being a female educator her mother's example motivated her to get higher education.

School Level

Michelle views that it is important to attend a school that has higher standards and to have a good teacher who believes in student's success.

Individual Level

Michelle resisted the opportunity gap that is linked to the race and gender by focusing on education to get higher education in science. She believed education was the key to success and independence. Michelle did not focus on what people think of her; instead, she focused on things that she enjoyed doing, which helped her to overcome the obstacles and achieve her goal in her life.

REFERENCES

Allexsaht-Snider, M., & Hart, L. (2001). Mathematics for all: How do we get there? *Theory Into Practice, 40*(2), 93–101.

Brenner, M. E. (1998). Adding cognition to the formula for culturally relevant instruction in mathematics. *Anthropology of Education Quarterly, 29*(2), 214–244.

Gutierrez, R. (1999). Advancing urban Latina/o youth in mathematics: Lessons from an effective high school mathematics department. *The Urban Review, 31*(3), 263–281.

Johnson, A., Brown, J., Carlone, H., Cuevas, A. K. (2011). Authoring identity amidst the treacherous terrain of science: A multiracial feminist examination of the journeys of three women of color in science. *Journal of Research in Science Teaching, 48*(4), 339–366.

Malloy, C. E., & Malloy, W. W. (1998). Issues of culture in mathematics teaching and learning. *The Urban Review 30*(3), 245–257.

Martin, D. B. (2000). *Mathematics success and failure among African-American youth: The roles of sociohistorical context, community forces, school influence, and individual agency.* Mahwah, NJ: Erlbaum

National Council of Teachers of Mathematics. (1989). *Curriculum and evaluation standards for school mathematics.* Reston, VA: National Council of Teachers of Mathematics.

National Council of Teachers of Mathematics. (2000). *Principles and standards for school mathematics.* Reston, VA: National Council of Teachers of Mathematics.

Ogbu, J. M (1992). Understanding cultural diversity and learning. *Educational Research, 21*(8), 5–14.

Secada, W. G. (1992). Race, ethnicity, social class, Language, and achievement in mathematics. In D. A. Grouws (Ed.), *Handbook of research on mathematics teaching and learning* (pp. 623–660). New York, NY: Macmillan.

Tate, W. F. (1997). Race, ethnicity, SES, gender, and language proficiency trends in mathematics achievement: An update. *Journal for Research in Mathematics Education, 28*(6), 652–679.

CHAPTER 8

LIFE IN THE DOUBLE BIND

An Investigation of How the Experiences of African American Females Influence Their Performance in Freshman Chemistry

Natasha Hillsman Johnson

The American Association for the Advancement of Science (AAAS) published its groundbreaking report *The Double Bind: The Price of Being a Minority Woman in Science* in April of 1976. It was highlighted in this report that the extent to which African American women in the sciences have historically faced challenges associated with both race and gender created what has been referred to as a double bind (Malcom, Hall, & Brown, 1976). I was born a year and a half later in the Fall of 1977, making me a member of the "next generation of scholars" seeking to understand the full impact of this double bind on African American females interest, persistence, and success in science, technology, engineering, and mathematics (STEM) careers. My perspective has been shaped by a variety of roles including as a STEM undergraduate student, practicing engineer, K–12 science teacher, and now as an

Women of Color In STEM, pages 125–138

education researcher. As an African American female immersed in a world of STEM, I can honestly say that I have lived my life in the "double bind." This chapter begins with an individual account of how I have experienced this double bind in my personal and professional life and how these experiences have shaped my work and educational research. Next, I will discuss my current research that examines the experiences of African American female undergraduate STEM students in freshman chemistry. Finally, I will share the preliminary research findings and implications for future research.

EXPERIENCES OF AN AFRICAN AMERICAN WOMAN IN A WORLD OF STEM

A few weeks ago, I received a call from my friend Michelle (pseudonym), who had recently started a new position as an online physics teacher. Having worked as an online science teacher, I understand the difficulty of this transition. Michelle shared that her first synchronous learning session had not gone as planned, but how surprised she was to learn that one of the parents had requested that their child be removed from her class. I could sense that she was hurt and a bit troubled by this experience. Michelle asked, "Have you ever felt as if you were treated differently by your students because you are an African American female?" Fortunately, I have been able to develop great relationships with my online students, and I have always been supported by my administration, but I admitted that I have often questioned the extent to which my race and/or gender has influenced my treatment and interaction during both casual encounters and professional settings. How many other women of color feel the same way? Thus setting the stage for the phenomenon that Malcom et al. (1976) has defined as the "double bind."

The Undergraduate Experience

While I am not the first individual in my family to attend and graduate from college, my socioeconomic status and ethnic background set me apart from other students at the Ivy League institution that I entered following graduation from high school. I was one of just two African American students (both females) out of a class of approximately 100 who graduated from my chemical engineering program. Feelings of isolation and inadequacy describe the years that I spent working on my undergraduate degree. I did not feel a connection with most of the other students or the faculty members. Differences in race, gender, and social class created what seemed like insurmountable barriers. One of my most vivid memories was one day when I was walking through the engineering building and my advisor walked by without speaking or acknowledging my presence. It was as if I was invisible, and this is how I felt most of the time. My major required a significant amount of time for laboratory work, problem sets, and other academic work. It was difficult to manage time for social events and time with friends because of pressures to perform academically. My positive memories relate mostly to work with the National Society of Black Engineers (NSBE) and my ability to mentor younger students. I developed my leadership skills on the executive board, eventually serving as president as well as a regional officer. This work gave me a sense of belonging and purpose on campus. It also connected me to students with similar experiences to my own. My undergraduate experience required many personal sacrifices; this is one of the many untold costs of the decision to persist in a STEM major. Was this experience characteristic of the STEM experience or a result of the double bind?

My Work as an Engineer

After graduation, I accepted a full-time engineering position with a utility company outside of Philadelphia, Pennsylvania. Historically, utility companies have been environments dominated by White males, so once again, I found myself as a bit of an anomaly. The feelings of isolation and inadequacy that began in college would continue as I began my professional career. In retrospect, I know that engineering work was not a good fit for my personality and interests, but at the time, I struggled to connect with my work and colleagues. Shortly after I arrived, one of the more seasoned engineers who was an African American female observed that I was not being offered the same level of support as the White male and White female new hires that started with me. There was a sadness, maybe a twinge of anger in her words, perhaps this experience was reminiscent of her own adjustment into the organization. I did not share her views, and I offered her a different perspective. The males shared common interests and hobbies, such as sports and cars. The older, White males could look at the younger White females and perhaps see a loved one, such as a sister, daughter, or spouse, and feel compelled to offer additional support. When they looked at me, there were barriers created not only by my race and gender, but also my age (and socioeconomic background), which created overwhelming obstacles in their ability to relate with me. Despite the efforts of an amazing engineering manager and a fantastic team, I never adjusted into the environment, and I resigned from my position almost two years to the date of my hire. Was this experience classic career uncertainty or a result of the double bind?

In the K–12 Classroom

I am not sure what initially sparked my interest in the teaching profession. Maybe it was my mother's love for her work as a teacher and her value of education. Maybe it was all the dedicated teachers who helped to encourage and motivate me. Whatever the reason, whenever I thought about careers that I might find more rewarding and fulfilling than engineering, teaching was always at the top of the list. When I moved to Atlanta, I began working with a little girl named McKenzie (pseudonym). McKenzie was 8 years old and attempting first grade for the third time. Not because she was not intelligent and not because she was not motivated, but simply because she had not attended school on a regular basis or received the additional assistance required at home. She faced many socioeconomic challenges of urban environments such as poor health care, limited preschool opportunities, and insufficient economic resources to provide for her basic needs. All of these problems served to distract her from obtaining the education she wanted and deserved. With the help of teachers, after-school programs, and an extensive support network, McKenzie's progress improved over the next few months. When I reflect on her journey, I feel a tremendous sense of accomplishment and fulfillment, something that was often missing in my engineering assignments. It was this experience that led me to apply and eventually join the Teach for America organization.

When I arrived in Houston for the summer training institute, it never occurred to me that I would be set apart because of my race and gender, but once again, I was the only African American and female on my corps team. My team of four was an amazing group of individuals who cared deeply about the African American and Latino youth in our summer school class, but the experience was a deeply personal one for me. When I looked around the classroom of children who had already experienced failure in this introductory high school science course, it was a confirmation that this work was too important for me not to be successful. When I looked around the classroom, I saw the faces of friends, relatives, former classmates, and I could also see myself. As I transitioned into my own classroom, as an African American female, I felt a great deal of pressure to relate with my students, manage disciplinary issues in my classroom, and make significant academic gains. The expectations of my students and administration seemed to be different or greater for me as an African American female. In essence, I perceived that I needed to be a perfect teacher. Was this my own insecurities or a result of the double bind?

STEM...the Second Time Around

In the years that I worked as a classroom teacher, I became a good, some might say a great, teacher. Despite all my knowledge and expertise, my hard work never seemed enough to make a real difference in the lives of my students. How could I confront the class-related achievement disparities and make a lasting impact on the quality of science education received by all children? I decided to pursue a doctoral degree in science education and aspired to become an education professor and researcher.

My first course as a full-time graduate student was a physical chemistry course. At the age of 32, when I entered the classroom, I was suddenly 17 again struggling with the same feelings of isolation and questioning my ability to compete as the only African American, female student in such a rigorous course. My questions posed to some chemistry faculty were met with condescending remarks. The classroom environments were focused purely on the acquisition of knowledge, with little regard for research-based instructional strategies to promote student learning. Although the culture and climate in STEM courses was the same, I was different. While I had failed my first quiz, my final grade in my chemistry course was an A–. My life and work experiences had made me a much more confident and self-directed learner. I was able to utilize my available resources and seek the necessary support. My experience as an adult learner in a STEM major helped me to select my dissertation research and what will undoubtedly become my life's work. My goal is to transform the climate of STEM courses and to work for systemic change in the quality of science instruction. Through my research, I hope to ensure all students, especially women and students of color, are provided the necessary support to not only survive but thrive in careers in the sciences. Were my aspirations a form of altruism or a result of the double bind?

Voices From STEM

For my dissertation research, I conducted a pilot study allowing me the opportunity to interview students, teaching assistants, and professors involved in the freshman chemistry course. One common theme that emerged from all of my research interviews was the need to change the culture and experience of the introductory chemistry course. It is my contention that the experiences of African American females in introductory science coursework has a profound impact on their persistence in STEM careers. Academic failure, regardless of your definition or reference frame, will impact just about everyone's life at some point in time. I have personally experienced academic difficulty from a number of perspectives. As a postsecondary student, my experience of academic difficulty damaged my self-esteem and forced me to reconsider my career as a chemical engineer. I have watched so many friends flee from majors in the sciences and forget about their dreams of becoming a doctor. As a teacher, my experience of academic difficulty has been to find the appropriate instructional strategies to meet the diverse needs of the students in my classroom, who are often defeated by the course content before the first day of class. As an aspiring researcher, my experience of academic difficulty has been to find a way to encourage the very brave students who are honest enough to sit down with me during a research interview and share their most personal experiences of academic difficulty in freshman chemistry. It is these experiences of academic difficulty that have shaped my interest in this research topic. I have often been criticized for the personal nature of my writing, but it is the faces of these individuals that motivate me to find additional strategies and resources to allow more young people to access STEM careers.

STATEMENT OF THE PROBLEM

Despite the rhetoric and emphasis placed on STEM education, over the past 50 years very little change has occurred in the areas of student interest and student performance in these fields. Although more students are pursuing postsecondary options than at any other time in the nation's history, student interest and enrollment in STEM majors has remained flat (National Science Board, 2014). Researchers have focused on improving the quality of science instruction at the K–12 level, recruitment of highly qualified teachers in critical need areas, and retention of undergraduate STEM students, especially women and underrepresented "minorities."

Tobias (1990) in her groundbreaking work, *They're Not Dumb, They're Different: Stalking the Second Tier*, described the undergraduate science student experience as follows:

> The proverbial look to the left, look to the right, two of your classmates will not be here after…may have first surfaced at Harvard Law School, but it certainly operates in introductory science where the first painful shakeout is expected to occur. (p. 10)

Seymour and Hewitt (1997) described the same "weed out" process experienced by a Black, male undergraduate engineering student. Attrition rates reflect that approximately 40% of STEM students will ultimately major in another discipline and, alarmingly, this rate is even higher for women and "minority" students (Seymour & Hewitt, 1997).

Attendance patterns indicate that over the past 3 decades, women's enrollment in higher education has outpaced their male counterparts (Zamani, 2003). In fact, women account for 56.3 % of undergraduate students (National Center for Education Statistics, 2002). Based on trends in the U.S. population, it is projected that by the year 2050, the majority of students on campus will be African Americans, Latinos, Native Americans, and Pacific Islanders (Hobbs & Stoops, 2000). As the number of students of color increases, colleges and universities must find a way to retain and graduate these students. According to Zamani (2003), African American females will receive nearly all the baccalaureate degrees awarded to African Americans by the year 2097.

According to Tai, Sadler, and Loehr (2005), chemistry is viewed as the central science, as mastery of its concepts is essential to further coursework in all of the sciences. Evidence for this belief lies in the order of coursework required at many major universities in the United States (p. 988). In this way, introductory chemistry serves as a gatekeeper to many careers in the sciences, which provides a rationale for understanding the key factors that contribute to success, failure, and overall preparation for introductory college chemistry. Although a gap exists in the literature, previous research indicates that factors contributing to success in college chemistry can be classified as demographic background, general education background, and previous science learning experiences (Tai, Sadler, & Loehr, 1995). While some factors are more easily controlled than others, they offer tremendous insight into why some students find a greater degree of success during the freshman chemistry experience. If we could better understand the experiences of academic difficulty of STEM majors in the freshman chemistry course, it would allow us to design appropriate interventions to increase student success and ultimately retention in STEM majors.

CONCEPTUAL FRAMEWORK

Attribution theory, developed by Bernard Weiner, has been recognized as one of the most influential cognitive theories with implications for academic motivation (Weiner, 1986). Attribution theory explains how people view the causes of their behaviors and those of others (Schunk, 2008). An attribution is defined as a perceived cause of a particular outcome. Attribution theory is grounded in Rotter's locus of control, which states that people seek to control important aspects of their lives (Schunk & Zimmerman, 2006). According to this theory, individuals either believe that outcomes are independent of behavior (external) or directly influenced by their behavior (internal). Locus of control is important in achievement contexts because expectancy beliefs are hypothesized to affect behavior. Students who believe they have control over their successes and failures should be more inclined to engage in academic tasks, expend effort, and persist than students who believe their behaviors have little impact on outcomes (Schunk, 2008). Attribution will also influence how learners respond to incidents of success and/or failure and future attempts at academic behaviors.

According to attribution theory, learners are strongly motivated by positive academic outcomes that allow them to feel good about themselves. Learners' self-perceptions will influence what factors the learner attributes personal success and/or failure. There are three dimensions used to explain success or failure: (a) internal versus external; (b) stable versus unstable; and (c) controllable versus uncontrollable. An internal factor originates within the individual and an external factor can be attributed to the environment. For example, one student might attribute performance on the chemistry examination to lack of preparation (internal), while another might attribute a poor grade to the design of the assessment (external). When learners believe an academic situation to be stable, they will anticipate the same outcome in the future. When learners believe an academic situation to be unstable, they will anticipate a different outcome. If we revisit the chemistry examination, one student anticipates poor performance on every test, while the other student expects the next test will be different. A controllable factor is one that can be easily altered if necessary, while an uncontrollable factor is perceived to not be easily altered. Students can study harder to ensure that they are well prepared for the next examination, but students cannot change their academic ability if they do not believe themselves capable of performing well in chemistry. According to attribution theory, students are most likely to perform well and persist in academic tasks if they attribute both their success and failures to internal, unstable factors that are within their control (Pintrich & Schunk, 2002). How many science majors have dropped a difficult course when they were capable of success? How many freshman students have been defeated by the abstract nature of chemical molecules or particulate nature of matter? Ultimately, it is the response to academic difficulty that will determine the future outcome for any particular student.

Externals consistently perform at a lower level in academic environments (Cappella & Weinstein, 2001), and African Americans are more likely to use external attributions and external locus of control (Friend & Neale, 1972; Weiner & Peter, 1973). Other research shows that when social class is controlled, these ethnic differences fade. According to Twenge, Zhang, and Im (2004), even after 40 years locus of control continues to be one of the most widely studied individual differences in psychology. According to attribution theory, such differences could have negative consequences for the academic behaviors and outcomes of African American students' performance and persistence in introductory chemistry courses.

SIGNIFICANCE OF STUDY

According to Malcom, Hall, and Brown (1976), African American women in the sciences have historically faced challenges associated with both race and gender, creating what has been referred to as a double bind. Programs designed to meet the needs of "minorities" or women, often fall short in meeting the needs of this unique population. Despite the progress of the past 35 years, disparities remain in degree attainment across many STEM disciplines (Malcom & Malcom, 2011). Additional research is needed to examine the individual and institutional factors that create obstacles to "minority" women choosing and succeeding in STEM fields (Malcom & Malcom, 2011, p. 165). The increasing numbers of African American female students in undergraduate programs coupled with the importance of mastery in the freshman chemistry course to future science study, makes this a vitally important area of research, particularly STEM programs hoping to attract and retain these individuals.

The purpose of this study is to understand how African American female undergraduate STEM students respond to academic difficulty while enrolled in the freshman chemistry course.

Specifically, this research will address the following questions:

1. How do African American female undergraduate STEM students describe their experiences of "academic difficulty" in the freshman chemistry course?
2. What are the characteristics of African American female undergraduate STEM students who struggle in freshman chemistry and later experience success?
3. What interventions are most successful in helping African American female undergraduate STEM students overcome academic barriers?

RESEARCH DESIGN

According to Bogdan and Biklen (2007), qualitative research is an umbrella terms that encompasses several research strategies that are typically defined by five common characteristics: (a) naturalistic, (b) descriptive data, (c) concern with process, (d) inductive, and (e) meaning. The *Merriam-Webster Dictionary* (n.d.) defines *naturalistic* as being characterized by a state or existence that is untouched by the influences of civilization or society. The researcher attempts to make meaning of the studied phenomenon through observation of events and people in a specific context. Unlike quantitative researchers, reliance on numbers and statistical analysis, qualitative research provides thick, rich descriptions using words and narratives. Great care is taken to preserve the voice of the participants in the study, who are often silenced or marginalized in other types of research. At the heart of qualitative research, is the desire of qualitative researchers to make meaning in the lives of others. This investigation is appropriate for qualitative inquiry because the goal is to understand how African American female undergraduate STEM students respond to academic difficulty experienced during the freshman chemistry course. The existing research, primarily quantitative in nature fails to give voice to students and share the distinctive challenges faced by African American females.

Data Collection

During the spring of 2012, three chemistry faculty members, three teaching assistants, and two undergraduate STEM students accepted the invitation to participate in this research study. Each participant was asked to sign an informed consent form explaining the research, their rights as a participant, as well as the risks and benefits of participation in the research study. Interviews were the primary source of information for this study. At the beginning of each interview, the researcher provided background information related to the research study and the researcher's own experiences as an STEM undergraduate student. This brief conversation was intended to build a rapport with the participants, thus allowing for a more candid and richer discussion about the research topic. I employed a semi-structured interview format with open-ended questions that allowed for greater flexibility during the process. Interviews addressed the following areas: previous academic experiences and outcomes, trajectories into STEM majors; description of study habits and academic behaviors; descriptions of STEM major environment/climate; academic strategies and interventions; and responses of friends, family members, and advisors to academic difficulty. All interviews were audio recorded and transcribed verbatim. Participants were asked to allow for follow-up interviews as needed.

Participant Selection and Description

From this larger group of participants, a smaller sample was selected for this research study. This purposeful sample was used in order to aid in the discovery and understanding of this topic. The first criterion was that the participants must be African American females. The second criterion for student participants was that they must be currently or recently enrolled in the introductory chemistry course and have a declared major in a science, technology, engineering, or mathematics (STEM) discipline. The third criterion was that they were currently or had recently performed below their level of expectations in the course.

The research participants, Terry and Nicole (pseudonyms) are both African American females. At the time of the interview both students were enrolled in the introductory chemistry course. Both had declared science majors, biology and chemistry, respectively and both intended to apply to medical school following completion of their undergraduate programs. Based on parental educational level and occupations, the student backgrounds could be described as middle class. The small number of African American female students enrolled in the course does not allow additional demographic information to be provided to ensure the confidentiality of the participants.

Data Analysis

Charmaz (2006) discussed, "We are part of the world we study and the data we collect. We construct our grounded theories through our past and present involvement and interactions with people, perspectives, and research practices" (p. 10). As a STEM graduate, chemistry educator, and education researcher, my personal experiences have and continue to shape this research and the lens through which I analyze my data. For this inductive analysis, I utilized the transcriptions from the semi-structured research interviews of two of the African American female STEM undergraduate students enrolled in the introductory freshman chemistry course. The qualitative data was read on paper and electronically, I also listened to the recordings to obtain a general description and reflect overall meaning, coded to generate categories, and themes from data (Charmaz, 2006; Creswell, 2007; Glaser & Strauss, 1967). Initial themes include (a) failure is not an option and (b) ineffective instructional strategies.

RESEARCH FINDINGS

Theme 1: Failure is Not an Option

Although the two women expressed different backgrounds, experiences, and trajectories into their science major, a theme of "failure is not an option" emerged. Both participants described their K–12 experiences as positive and expressed a value for education and a love of learning. For the purpose of this investigation, academic difficulty was defined as performance below their level of expectations in the course. As the researcher, I was surprised when the participants revealed that they had earned semester grades of an A– and a B in the first semester course. In the fall of 2013, there were approximately 1,870 students enrolled in freshman chemistry. Approximately 350 students withdrew from the course, while another 150 earned a final course grade of a D or F. The grade distribution for this semester was 33% A, 34% B, 22% C, 8% D, and 4% F. These data are consistent with the course performance during the Fall of 2012, indicating that both students performed relatively well in the course. Terry and Nicole both expressed a sentiment that they did not live up to their potential (usually in reference to course examinations) with statements such as, "I could have earned an A" or "I don't like failing myself" or "I should study better." Both participants made it clear that they held themselves to only the highest of standards leading me to conclude that for each of them failure was not an option.

Theme 2: Ineffective Instructional Strategies and Design

Regardless of any personal level of success in the course, both participants shared a belief that the instructional strategies used in the introductory course were not effective. Students discussed the number of students who did not regularly attend lectures, and the viewpoint of the students who did attend that it was not helpful in their learning of the content. When asked about course lectures, Nicole responded, "I do not learn from lecture, not at all." Terry described course lectures as "a waste of time" and "not interactive or motivating." Students cited motives such as bonus points or advantages on course examinations as reasons to attend lecture. Both participants expressed concerns with online systems used for homework and course examinations. They also thought that smaller classes and lectures that incorporated real world applications would be beneficial to students. For the most part, participants believed that students were expected to grasp the connection between the laboratory component and course lecture themselves. Finally, Terry and Nicole described the chemistry professors as being out of touch as it relates to the difficulty level of the content and having unrealistic expectations for students' interest and time available to complete chapter reading, work problems, and study for the course. Both students offered solutions to make significant changes to the instructional design and delivery of the introductory chemistry courses.

FINAL THOUGHTS

Unfortunately, few school leaders, educators, and researchers truly understand what is necessary to create the kind of high quality instruction that promotes and sustains student interest in the sciences. This lack of quality science instruction has huge implications for the upward mobility and social equality of African American students and underserved communities. There continues to be an absence of African American parental and community role models who have experienced success in (STEM) professions.

Historically, African American have been underrepresented in mathematics and science careers. For over 25 years, African Americans have continued to make up less than 2% of actual practicing PhD-holding scientists (National Science Board, 2000). Even though African American students tend to gravitate towards careers in the social sciences and education, there are still only a small percentage of African Americans employed as science teachers in the United States. As we continue to search for answers to the greatest science and technological questions of the 21st century, African Americans remain an "untapped talent" with "unlimited potential" to offer innovative solutions to these most important problems (Russell, 2005).

There exists a profound gap in the current literature as it relates to African American female students learning in the sciences at the elementary, secondary, and postsecondary levels. This chapter has attempted to explore how African American female undergraduate STEM students respond to academic difficulty while enrolled in the freshman chemistry course. The findings reported are preliminary and this research is ongoing. Additional research is needed to examine how historical, social, cultural, economic, and psychological factors work together to influence the interest and persistence of African Americans females in the area of STEM careers. There is a great deal to be learned from the voices of African American female STEM undergraduate students, who have for too long been silenced, marginalized, and oppressed in their academic institutions. As I conclude this analysis, I have one lingering question: Why did these two young ladies who had performed so well in the introductory chemistry course feel compelled to share their story with me? Was this a consequence of greater concern for the freshman chemistry program or a result of their own lived experiences in the double bind?

REFERENCES

Bogdan, R. C., & Biklen, S. K. (2007). *Qualitative research for education: An introduction to theories and methods.* New York, NY: Pearson.

Cappella, E., & Weinstein, R. S. (2001). Turning around reading achievement: Predictors of high school students' academic resilience. *Journal of Educational Psychology, 93*(4), 758.

Charmaz, K. (2006). *Constructing grounded theory: A Practical guide through qualitative analysis.* Washington, DC: SAGE.

Creswell, J. W. (2007). *Qualitative inquiry & research design: Choosing among five approaches.* Thousand Oaks, CA: SAGE.

Friend, R., & Neale, J. (1972). Children's perceptions of success and failure: An attributional analysis of the effects of race and social class. *Developmental Psychology, 7*(2), 124–128.

Glaser, B. G., & Strauss, A. L. (1967). *Discovery of grounded theory: Strategies for qualitative research.* Chicago, IL: Aldine.

Hobbs, F., & Stoops, N. (2002). *Demographic trends in the 20th century: Census 2000 special reports.* Washington, DC: U.S. Census Bureau. Retrieved from https://www.census.gov/prod/2002pubs/censr-4.pdf

Malcom, S. M., Hall, P. Q., & Brown, J. W. (1976). *The double bind: The price of being a minority woman in science.* Washington, DC: American Association for the Advancement of Science.

Malcom, L. E., & Malcom, S. M. (2011). The double bind: The next generation. *Harvard Educational Review, 81*(2), 162–172.

Merriam-Webster. (n.d.). Naturalistic. In *Merriam-Webster.com dictionary.* Retrieved 2018 from https://www.merriam-webster.com/dictionary/naturalistic

National Center for Education Statistics. (2002). *The condition of education 2002.* Washington, DC: Office of Educational Research and Improvement, U.S. Department of Education.

National Science Board. (2000). *Science and engineering indicators 2000* (NSB-00-1). Arlington, VA: National Science Foundation.

Pintrich, P. R., & Schunk, D. H. (2002). *Motivation in education: Theory, research, and applications* (2nd ed.). Upper Saddle River, NJ: Pearson.

Russell, M. L. (2005). Untapped talent and unlimited potential: African American students and the science pipeline. *The Negro Educational Review, 56*(2/3), 167–182.

Seymour, E., & Hewitt, N. (1997). *Talking about leaving: Why undergraduates leave the sciences.* Boulder, CO: Westview.

Schunk, D. H. (2008). *Learning theories: An educational perspective.* Upper Saddle River, NJ: Pearson.

Schunk, D. H., & Zimmerman, B. J. (2006). Competence and control beliefs: Distinguishing the means and ends. In P. A. Alexander & P. H. Winne (Eds), *Handbook of educational psychology* (2nd ed.; pp. 349–367). Mahwah, NJ: Erlbaum.

Tai, R. H., Sadler, P. M., & Loehr, J. F. (2005). Factors influencing success in introductory college chemistry. *Journal of Research in Science Teaching, 42*(9), 987–1012.

Tobias, S. (1990). *They're not dumb, they're different: Stalking the second tier.* Tuscon, AZ: Research Corporation.

Twenge, J. M., Zhang, L., & Im, C. (2004). It's beyond my control: A cross-temporal meta-analysis of increasing externality in locus of control, 1960–2002. *Personality and Social Psychology Review, 8*(3), 308–319.

Weiner, B. (1986). *An attributional theory of motivation and emotion.* New York, NY: Springer.

Weiner, B., & Peter, N. (1973). A cognitive-developmental analysis of achievement and moral judgments. *Developmental Psychology, 9*(3), 290–309.

Zamani, E. M. (2003). African American women in higher education. *New Directions for Student Services, 2003*(104): 5–18. https://doi.org/10.1002/ss.109

CHAPTER 9

MAKING STEM REAL FOR AFRICAN AMERICAN FEMALE PRESERVICE SCIENCE TEACHERS

Issues of Learning and Teaching in Science and Math Education Courses in Virginia

Clair Berube
Melva Grant
Patti Horne-Hastings
SueAnn McKinney

The future of science education is intricately linked to the future of America. If the United States is to maintain its standing as a world leader and leading economy, a well-trained STEM (science, technology, engineering, and mathematics) workforce will be needed. President Obama has made STEM initiatives a priority. According to the White House Blog (Locke, 2011), "Initiatives like Race to the Top and the 'Educate to Innovate' campaign demonstrate the administration's ongoing commitment to making sure

Women of Color In STEM, pages 139–157
Copyright © 2021 by Information Age Publishing

Americans get the science and technology skills they need to fill the jobs of the future. *STEM: Good Jobs Now and for the Future*, by Commerce's Economics and Statistics Administration, shows that growth in STEM jobs has been three times greater than that of non-STEM jobs over the last 10 years. And throughout the next decade, STEM occupations are projected to grow by 17%, compared to 9.8% growth for other occupations. This growth underlines why this administration has made a $206 million commitment toward STEM training and related programs in the 2012 budget.

The Committee on Science, Space, and Technology House of Representatives (2011) recognized that STEM education needed to be fortified to promote innovation, inquiry, discovery, and exploration. They believe that this effort would warrant the "economic strength and competitiveness in the international marketplace of the 21st century" (Committee on Science, 2011, p. 5). President Obama further supported the cause by appealing the need for the preparation of STEM educators with sound content knowledge and teaching methodologies that are effective, innovative, and promote problem-solving and discovery instruction (Committee on Science, 2011). Further, Obama (2009) and Bracey (2009) stated that when innovation and creativity are supported and highlighted during instruction, the potential for failing returns can be eliminated (Obama, 2009; Bracey as cited in Obama, 2009, p. 81).

President Obama's "Educate to Innovate" initiative promotes the ideals of intensifying the efforts to promote STEM literacy, so that our nation's students can

> learn deeply and think critically in science, math, engineering, and technology; move American students from the middle of the pack to the top in the next decade; and expand STEM education and career opportunities for underrepresented groups, including women and girls. (Committee on Science, 2011, p. 5)

Although the Department of Education and the National Science Foundation proposed investing over $100 million to sustenance STEM education, Kendricks and Arment (2011) reported that the number of African Americans partaking in STEM education and careers, have not shown a substantial increase. In an effort to contend with this lack of representation of subgroups pursuing STEM education and careers, many school districts have shifted from just providing STEM education opportunities in the middle and high schools where content knowledge is separated, and have begun to offer STEM education in the elementary grades where curiosity and enthusiasm is more profound, and content knowledge can be more easily integrated.

In comparison to their non-STEM counterparts, STEM workers of all races earn 26% more on average and are less likely to experience joblessness.

Meanwhile, STEM degree holders enjoy higher earnings, regardless of their occupation. And no matter what their major, college graduates who work in a STEM job enjoy an earnings premium (Locke, 2011). However, Morella (2013) reported as many as 60% of high school students who begin in STEM are giving up on STEM fields by graduation time.

How will we win these brilliant young minds and lure them from other occupations? The key lies in K–8 science and mathematics education in American public schools; hooking kids when they are young on STEM topics and nurturing in them a love for science and math. Individuals begin to develop perceptions and knowledge of STEM prior to and during their elementary education (NRC, 2007), which increases the importance of teaching STEM at the elementary level. Further, capitalizing on young learners' innate interest in STEM at the elementary level (Maltese & Tai, 2010) can stimulate their desire to learn more about STEM (NRC, 2011). The potential gains and influence of quality STEM curriculum and instruction at the elementary level provides justification for supporting efforts to increase elementary teachers' capacity to teach STEM. Teachers with negative attitudes toward STEM tend to avoid teaching STEM (Appleton, 2003), and such attitudes of the teacher are frequently transferred to their students (Deemer, 2004). Thus, it appears that poor attitudes toward STEM may be initiated and enhanced by teachers.

INTRODUCTION TO PROBLEM-BASED LEARNING PEDAGOGY

Berube (2014) reported on students who were African American, and all of them were women during the semester of the study. They took science and mathematics education courses in preparation to teach either elementary science or math, or secondary science or math in a middle or high school. Nowadays, many schools employ blocks of STEM time, where teachers use problems or scenarios to teach concepts. Science and math are not taught as separate subjects in these cases, but as STEM; integrated science, technology, engineering, and math together. Science education professors across the country have been searching for a better way to teach future teachers how to teach science for a long time, since the age of lecturing to science students is over. Preservice teachers (college students studying to become teachers) want to know the latest pedagogical techniques and research in order to be the best STEM teachers they can be. Problem-based learning (PBL) using inquiry has been successful in raising preservice teachers self-efficacy and confidence (and by doing so, enjoyment) in teaching science and mathematics (Thomas, Horne, Donnelly, & Berube, 2013). PBL is a pedagogical practice that helps people who are uncomfortable with science feel more comfortable and competent in teaching science.

Haberman (1995, 2005) has done much research on STAR teachers who have employed PBL and has identified STAR teachers as those who possess 15 traits that make them exceptional: Teachers value learning, teachers are persistent and consistently pursue strategies and activities so that students can meet with success, teachers take responsibility for student's learning, teachers can relate theory into practice, teachers develop rapport with students, teachers can handle bureaucracy, teachers take responsibility for their mistakes, teachers have emotional and physical stamina, teachers are organized, teachers model hard work and stamina, teachers respect differences, teachers engage in active teaching, teachers make students feel needed, teachers put children first, and teachers have gentleness in a violent society. STAR teachers suffer less burnout and are more successful. They also employ problem-based learning in their teaching of STEM.

Haberman (2009) reported that a special needs child has a greater opportunity to graduate from high school when compared to an African American child who faces two or more teachers during any academic year in an urban district due to teacher turnover. In order for urban districts to comply with the mission of increasing subgroups in STEM education and possible careers, it is essential that educators first address the concern of the provision of equitable education opportunities for minorities, especially African American girls who attend urban schools, and the provision of teachers who are a master at their craft. Although we argue that the inclusion of PBL opportunities during instruction is one approach and strategy for fostering an interest and perhaps, possible increased student achievement in the STEM fields, without a commitment to this approach, and to the necessary ideology to meet success in urban, high-poverty environments, teachers may possibly just go through the motions, without the necessary conviction.

"Real teaching" is how Haberman (1995, 2005) referred to this conviction that is necessary during instruction of any kind but is particularly that is needed to foster an interest in STEM education. Real teaching refers to the belief that teachers feel in regards to their responsibility to truly motivate, interest, and engage the students in learning opportunities that incorporate the experiences of the students. Without this conviction, many teachers resort to the directive acts of a "pedagogy of poverty," a term coined by Haberman (1991, 2005), that refers to the simple practice of giving information, seatwork, busy work, and low-level learning. Unfortunately, this practice permeates many urban schools and classrooms affecting the learning opportunities for African American students. In union with the function of real teaching, teachers must also comply with the notion of "you and me against the material," another function that refers to the belief system and conviction needed by teachers to effectively implement problem-based learning during STEM instruction. This function centers on the practice of putting the material to be learned first, and the needs of the child second. The continued cycle of this practice leads children to experience failure and has the potential of instilling within students that they are not capable of learning specific content material (Haberman, 1995, 2005). In contrast, effective teachers believe, as stated best by Haberman (1995):

> It is us, we together, joined in a common effort, against the material, which can sometimes be tricky or difficult or more complicated than it seems. But we can do it together and both derive a sense of joy and well-being: you-the student-because of the thrill that comes from learning and me-the teacher-because I helped create a situation that will enable you to succeed. (p. 86)

When these convictions are rooted within problem-based learning during science instruction, students are more apt to meet success in STEM education.

Berube (2014) reported, "National efforts have been in place to transform the mathematics classroom into one that supports STEM education, learning communities, and inquiry-driven instruction, and moving away from traditional approaches, such as procedural knowledge and memorization of algorithms" (i.e., Hiebert, 2003; Manouchehri, 2004; National Council of Teachers of Mathematics, 2000, 2007). Although these national efforts have been supported and articulated by the NCTM, many urban, high-poverty school districts continue to fall short. According to Lubienski (2001), the pedagogy of urban teachers is not consistent with the recommendations proposed by the NCTM, which, in turn, will impact STEM instruction and methodologies. For example, McKinney, Bol, and Berube (2010) investigated the mathematics instructional practices of star teachers in urban, high-poverty schools, and concluded that star teachers use a variety of approaches and practices that are culturally relevant and support NCTM's principles. These teaching practices include asking higher level questions, adding personal creativity, differentiating instruction, and using cooperative groups, manipulatives, hands-on and problem-based learning activities (McKinney, Bol, & Berube, 2010; as cited in Berube, 2014, p. 33). Yet, a question remains: "Is there a cultural component that may be holding back African-Americans in STEM fields?"

SCIENTIFIC LITERACY AND FAITH

Throughout the ages, humans have asked the important questions of existence, such as where did we come from and why are we here? Many people have chosen to answer these questions with spiritual answers, which we are free to do; however, scientific questions demand scientific answers and humans have been asked to make the false choice between religion and science for centuries. Science by definition requires objective observation and documentation of these observations via reliable and valid measurement instruments. Science is not open to opinion or subjectivity. Because of this objectivity, science is considered one of the best ways to arrive at the truth which we seek when we ask questions about the universe. However, many people of all races have religious backgrounds which may prevent them from objectively participating in STEM.

In a report on STEM education in the great American urban public school system, Berube (2014) noted two concerns with religion and science. Berube is a professor at an HBCU and teaches mostly African American upper middle to middle class students in the school of education. Early on, it was noticed that many of the students (the large majority of whom are young women) were not being drawn to science at the same rate as the Caucasian students had been at other universities, so a point was made to try to find out why. It did not seem to have anything to do with an "anti-intellectual" climate found in so much of America today, but it did seem to have something to do with religion and/or "faith." Also encountered was a suspicion or lack of trust in science as a reliable source of information about our world.

Every semester, Berube taught evolution, and every semester there were debates in class about this topic. Berube (2014) stated:

> As a professor who teaches science to pre-service teachers, I have run across certain difficulties from time to time in my science teaching. The problem stems from beliefs that some students have about religion that prevent them from accepting scientific explanations about phenomena. For example, evolution seems to ignite controversy because some students don't believe that the earth has been found to be 4.54 billion years old. According to the Bible, it is only about 6,000 years old. If your parent is a minister, or if you adhere to a strict Biblical interpretation of the world, then you may have a problem with science. I am not saying here that one shouldn't be allowed to live in a free country and to believe however they choose; I am saying that science demands objective scrutiny. This mindset can hold back scientific progress in America. (p. 13)

While I focused this chapter on African American women, this trend can also be seen in religious people of all races and walks of life. However, according to the Pew Research Religion and Public Life Project (2013),

> Of all the major racial and ethnic groups in the United States, black Americans are the most likely to report a formal religious affiliation. Even among those blacks who are unaffiliated, three-in-four belong to the "religious unaffiliated" category (that is, they say that religion is either somewhat or very

important in their lives), compared with slightly more than one-third of the unaffiliated population overall. (para. 19)

Scientific literacy is vital if America is to maintain its lead as a STEM powerhouse. Especially since minorities will be the majority in America by 2043 (Kayne, 2013).

SCIENTIFIC LITERACY AND AFRICAN AMERICAN WOMEN

One of the most important subtypes of literacy is scientific literacy. Scientific literacy is an important reason that we need all Americans buying into science. According to the American Association for the Advancement of Science (1990),

> Without a science-literate population, the outlook for a better world is not promising. Most Americans are not science-literate. One only has to look at the international studies of educational performance to see that U.S. students rank near the bottom in science and mathematics—hardly what one would expect if the schools were doing their jobs well. (1990, para. 11)

As for the connection between race and religion: the question becomes; how does religious identification and literal interpretation of religious texts influence scientific literacy? Darren Sherkat (2011) wrote an article entitled "Religion and Scientific Literacy in the United States" in which he examined how adherence to strict religious dogma affects scientific literacy. Independent variables included sectarian and Catholic identifications, no identifications, and the importance of fundamentalist versus secular beliefs about the Bible and other religious books, education, income, race, region, and gender. The dependent variable (scientific literacy) was measured using the 2006 General Social Survey (GSS; p. 1135). Sherkat cites research (Berkman, Pacheco, & Plutzer, 2008; Darnell & Sherkat, 1997; Ellison & Musick, 1995; Lienesch, 2007) that states "Christian fundamentalist beliefs are rooted in the position that Christian sacred texts are inerrant, and should be taken as true representations of earth and human history" (Sherkat, 2011, p. 1136). As I mentioned earlier, literal interpretations of the Bible can affect how a person learns or doesn't learn science.

Sectarian Protestant denominations include the Southern Baptist Convention, Church of Christ, and Assembly of God. These groups have been at the forefront of opposition to teaching about evolution (Sherkat, 2011, p. 1137). And again, when speaking about race and religion, it has been mentioned that most African Americans belong to religious groups. According to Sehgal and Smith with the Pew Forum on Religion and Public Life, Blacks are more religious on a variety of measures than the U.S.

population as a whole (Sehgal & Smith, 2009). Seventy-eight percent of African-Americans are Protestant (compared with 50% of the general population), 40% of these claiming to be Baptist; 5% Catholic, and less than half a percentage point are atheists.

> By several measures, including importance of religion in life, attendance at religious services and frequency of prayer, the historically black Protestant group is among the most religiously observant traditions. In fact, on these and other measures of religious practices and beliefs, members of historically black Protestant churches tend to resemble members of evangelical Protestant churches, another highly religious group. (Seghal & Smith, 2009, para. 8)

What are the implications of this research? Studies show that STEM careers are the jobs of the future (Basso, 2012; Carnegie Science Center, 2012; Engler, 2012; Locke, 2011; Langdon et al., 2012). According to Locke, "STEM jobs help America win the future" from The White House blog) "In comparison to their non-STEM counterparts, STEM workers earn 26 percent more on average and are less likely to experience joblessness. Meanwhile, STEM degree holders enjoy higher earnings, regardless of their occupation. And no matter what their major, college graduates who work in a STEM job enjoy an earnings premium" (Locke, 2011).

Studies also show that AfricanAmericans are underrepresented in STEM fields (Loftus, 2012; Payton, 2004; Palmer et al., 2010). In addition to the factors presented in Chapter 3 in the discussion of high-needs urban schools, could religiosity and belief systems be a determining factor in the low rates of African-Americans in STEM fields? It is vital that the brain-drain of African Americans from STEM fields is halted, and it is very important that a possible contributing source of African American underrepresentation in STEM is recognized and dealt with, no matter how politically incorrect or unpleasant. This holds for all groups whose religious beliefs stand in the way of scientific progress. The inability of much of America to reconcile religion or belief systems with science is a problem not found in other industrialized countries. "In order to maintain American competitiveness, we must be able to let the evidence lead the way. The jobs of the future demand it. We cannot afford to leave anyone behind" (Berube, 2013, pp. 16, 17).

If we can assume that religiosity is one factor that may be preventing African American women from considering STEM as a job option, what can be done about it? Can we change the idea that STEM is only for a certain type of person and not for others? Can certain teaching pedagogical practices (PBL) change the minds of African American preservice teachers to the point where they can envision STEM careers in teaching? The authors believe so.

Teachers can have huge effects on whether African American female students avoid STEM fields. One may look at how a teacher's actions or inactions impact the likelihood that a student will enter the STEM pipeline. For instance, if the elementary teacher lacks confidence in science, she spends less time on it and demonstrates less passion for it. This will impact how her students view science. Also, a teacher's perceptions about the abilities of subgroups or the teachers' own subconscious views of a scientist may unintentionally influence the degree of expectations she holds for students of color and/or females creating a double whammy for African American women. The self-fulfilling prophecy comes in to play when teachers track African American females in lower level STEM courses leading many African American females to doubt their own efficacy in those fields. Also, if the teacher fails to show students a variety of occupations in STEM, African American females may not see a career of interest to them. Fortunately, PBL has been shown to raise science self-efficacy in preservice teachers (Thomas et al., 2013).

What Is Problem-Based Learning?

Problem-based learning (PBL) is the method that the authors believe will transform STEM teaching in the future and raise the confidence and competence of teachers who teach STEM content areas. It incorporates all four STEM subjects into one problem-solving activity, instead of teaching science, technology, engineering, and math as separate subjects, and more accurately reflects real-world STEM. According to Donna Sterling (2007), former professor of science education at George Mason University in Fairfax Virginia,

> In problem-based instruction, students are presented with a realistic science dilemma, such as the sudden appearance and spread of an unknown disease in a fictional town. Students work collaboratively to research the problem, conduct hands-on activities to learn more about it, incorporate "new" information on the topic (made available through teacher-provided "news flashes"), and eventually make informed recommendations for solving the problem based on their findings. In this way, students are modeling the processes of science and connecting their learning to a real context. (p. 50)

Berube (2014) states, "Problem-based learning (Hmelo-Silver, 2004) has been shown to increase student learning by both engaging in finding solutions to real-life problems using science (Sterling & Hargrove 2012), and prompting them to use higher-order thinking skills" (p. 74). Students who have engaged in PBL experiences such as VISTA (Virginia Initiative for Science Teaching and Achievement, n.d.) have been shown to score more highly on science achievement tests. As Sterling, Matkins, Frazier, and Logerwell (2010) have shown, not only is PBL sound pedagogy, it is also instrumental in providing marginalized students a learning environment that springboards their learning to close achievement gaps in science, technology, and mathematics (VISTA, n.d.). PBL embeds scientific content into real-world problems for the students to solve, and in doing so, turns students into engineers, researchers, scientists, and mathematicians.

According to Thomas et al. (2013), "PBL implementation in the K–12 setting has more recently gained international attention as a way to provide creative inquiry that fosters critical thinking and is aligned with students' interests and abilities" (Thomas et al., 2013, p. 95, as cited in Delisle, 1997). It is a learning approach that allows for individual flexibility in learning and the social construction of knowledge. Aligned with Vygotsky's theory of constructivism, PBL pushes students to connect prior knowledge with a current problem and solve it in their own way. PBL supports the American Association for the Advancement of Science (AAAS; 1993), the National Research Council's (NRC; 2011), and the Virginia Mathematics and Science Coalition's (VMSC; 2010) visions inquiry-based and student-centered science. VISTA researchers defined PBL as "students solving a complex problem with multiple solutions over time like a scientist in a real-world-context" (VISTA, 2011). They further stated the problem must be meaningful to students and is typically embedded in a course of study 1 to 5 weeks in duration (VISTA, 2011). Through PBL, students ask scientific questions relevant to their lives, collect evidence, and develop explanations based on the evidence obtained. This type of inquiry provides students with the highest level of investigative control, unlike traditional teacher-led explorations (Bell, Smetana, & Binns, 2005). Students use the problem-solving cycle as a roadmap throughout their PBL investigations (Sterling at VISTA, 2011). "Contrary to the lockstep myth of the scientific method, the problem-solving cycle allows students the flexibility to move forward or retrace their steps in the investigation as needed. This enables student researchers to backtrack in response to new information gained and better represents the way scientists work to find solutions in their profession" (Berube, Dash, & Thomas-Charles, 2019, p. 3).

PBL has many benefits for students, including in the affective domain. Increased confidence combined with culturally sensitive pedagogy, creates greater interest and more positive views of science among PBL participants (Sterling, Matkins, Frazier, & Logerwell, 2007). In the cognitive domain, Frazier and Sterling (2008) found that "students experience significant growth in their science content knowledge and skills" while employing PBL (p. 115). Social skills were improved also, and according to Tarhan and Acar (2007), students in a PBL class were more motivated, self-confident, willing to problem-solve and share knowledge, and were more active in cooperative groups than students of traditional instruction.

METHODS

Implementing PBL/Inquiry in a Teacher Education Program

Little research has been conducted to investigate the effects of PBL on both quantitative and qualitative outcomes of African American preservice science teachers. Two of the authors (Horne and Berube) have previously conducted research with science education faculty from across the state of Virginia (Thomas, Horne, Donnelly, & Berube, 2013) in a quantitative study that addressed how infusing PBL into science methods courses influenced preservice science teacher self-efficacy. Most of the subjects of the prior study were White. The nine African American subjects were included in the larger pool of subjects and the results analyzed. In this chapter, the author delves deeper into the results of those African American subjects and includes qualitative data from current African American students to seek the answers to questions not addressed in the previous study. The authors will also examine the unique problems and challenges of their current African American students who are currently enrolled in their science methods courses.

As with the White subjects, PBL and lessons were implemented as a pedagogical technique to African American preservice teachers attending a mid-Atlantic HBCU in either an elementary, or a secondary science course. The study was implemented in fall 2011 (Thomas et al., 2013).

Participants

Participants for the quantitative study were African American preservice science teachers at a mid-Atlantic HBCU. During the fall of 2011, there were 9 African American preservice teachers pretested and 5 posttested. This portion of the study had previously taken place as part of the research study conducted by Thomas et al. (2013) and results were previously published. For the qualitative portion of this study, participants of the study were elementary science education students at the mid-Atlantic HBCU, during the fall semester of 2014. Descriptive data concerning the African American students pulled from the quantitative study (Thomas et al., 2013) are shown in Table 9.1.

TABLE 9.1 Demographic Data for Pre-Test (N = 9) and Post-Test (N = 5)		
Demographic	Pre-Test N	Post-Test N
African-American	9	5

QUANTITATIVE RESEARCH QUESTIONS

In order to gather the information necessary, the following research questions helped guide the research:

1. What are African American preservice teachers' perceptions of delivering PBL?
2. Will science self-efficacy show statistically significant gains as a result of the treatment of PBL pedagogy?

Instrumentation

Science Self-Efficacy

It is believed by the researchers that African American preservice science teachers may have low self-efficacy in their confidence in teaching science. Studies also show that PBL raises confidence:

> Teachers who lack confidence and comfort with a student-centered approach tend to fall back on traditional modes of teaching leading to marginal learning (Osborne, Collins, & Simon, 2003). Teachers who were trained in PBL and provided with on-going coaching showed improved confidence in their ability to use problem-based instruction (Etherington, 2003). (Thomas et al., 2013, p. 97)

Part of this study included quantitative data gathered as a result of pre and posttesting African American preservice teachers at the HBCU using the STEBI B instrument to see if PBL increased the students' science self-efficacy.

> Participants completed a survey developed by Enochs and Riggs (1990) known as the Science Teaching Efficacy Belief Instrument (STEBI-B). "The STEBI-B developed a survey to evaluate pre-service teachers' self-efficacy towards teaching science. The instrument was based around Bandura's (1977) social learning theory. The instrument consists of two constructs: personal science teaching efficacy (PSTE) and science teaching outcome expectancy (STOE). The STEBI-B has a reliability rating of .90 (PSTE) and .76 (STOE) making it a reliable instrument. The instrument consists of five Likert items, ranging from *strongly agree* to *strongly disagree* across the continuum. Enochs and Riggs (1990) suggests that the following numbers, 5 = *strongly agree*, 4 = *agree*, 3 = *undecided*, 2 = *disagree*, and 1 = *strongly disagree*, to correspond with responses. (Thomas et al., 2013, p. 100)

Procedure

Over the course of the Fall 2011 semester, African American students at a mid-Atlantic HBCU were given the STEBI-B as a benchmark to complete at the beginning of each semester before methodology instruction. Students had the opportunity to conduct PBL labs and also to create their own PBL units. The STEBI-B was administered again during the final week of the course in order to detect and measure any changes in science self-efficacy as a result of the PBL treatment.

Analysis of Results

Both descriptive statistics and analysis of variance (ANOVA) were conducted to address the research questions. Results of the previous study, in which the African American students were participants, showed that PBL did indeed raise preservice teacher science self-efficacy. Research Question 1: "What are preservice teachers' perceptions of delivering PBL? To address this question, the researchers conducted descriptive statistics to display preservice teachers' perceptions prior to the delivery of coursework towards teaching PBL and after the coursework was completed. Prior to coursework, preservice teachers scored towards undecided ($M = 3.53$, $SD = .539$) on personal science teaching efficacy (PSTE) and moderately low as well on science teaching outcome expectancy (STOE; $M = 3.50$, $SD = .437$). For preservice teachers, results from the posttest suggest that preservice students perceived themselves to be moderately high in personal science teaching efficacy (PSTE; $M = 4.13$, $SD = .413$) as a result of the coursework. Furthermore, while their science teaching outcome expectancy (STOE) was not as high ($M = 3.87$, $SD = .564$), there was small gain from the pretest. Moreover, the effect size, using Cohen's d, was computed to identify practical significance of the differences between the pretest and posttest (Cohen, 1988). The pretest and posttest revealed strong effects on PSTE ($d = 1.019$) and STOE ($d = 1.109$). Means, standard deviations, and effect size are displayed in Table 9.2.

TABLE 9.2 Descriptive Statistics on Pre-Test (N = 29) and Post-Test (N = 25)

	Pre-Test		Post-Test		Effect Size
Subscale	*M*	*SD*	*M*	*SD*	*d*
PSTE	3.53	.539	4.13	.413	1.019*
STOE	3.50	.437	3.87	.564	1.109*

Note: Effect size strength were determined using Cohen's (1988) breakdown for small ($d = .20 - .49$), moderate ($d = .50 - .79$), or strong ($d = .80$ or higher).

* Strong effect.

SUMMARY

Data revealed that students initially did not perceive themselves as capable of delivering PBL prior to their training. The participants were undecided on whether they could perform PBLs at an acceptable level. However, the data did reveal that the coursework improved their understanding of PBL and enhanced their self-efficacy towards delivering this method of instruction in a science class. Furthermore, preservice teachers felt they were capable of getting their future students to obtain student outcomes towards PBL (Thomas et al., 2013, pp. 101–102).

Qualitative Study

In order to delve deeper into this research, Dr. Berube presented her current (Fall 2014) African American elementary science education students an informal qualitative survey, called "Preservice Science and Mathematics Education Qualitative Survey" (see Appendix). The purpose of this survey was to ask deep questions in the affective domain concerning the African American science students' feelings about science that could not be gleaned from a quantitative measurement instrument. Questions include items such as, "As an African American, have you faced obstacles that your White classmates did not have to face? If so, what were they?"

Results and Discussion of Preservice Science and Mathematics Education Qualitative Survey

The students given the survey were taking Dr. Berube's science for children class—a course for elementary education majors. The class was small; 7 students, but they represented the School of Education student body in general. One student was a pre-engineering major and was taking the class as an elective. The rest were taking the class as a requirement for their elementary education major. The survey was given informally to get a general idea of the attitudes of the students to STEM in general and to the teaching of science and math, and to guide discussion.

It was not surprising that the preengineering major *would have been* looking forward to teaching science and math if she were going into teaching. She also mentioned that she was excited by the class and might switch her major to education. This student mentioned that during her K–12 education, many of her teachers were surprised that an African American student was excelling in math and science. This "stereotype" that many teachers have of minorities in math and science is not new. Claude Steele published famous articles (1995, 1997) on the effects of high-stakes testing on populations with a lot to lose. In Steele and Aronson's 1995 paper "The Effects of

Stereotype Threat on the Standardized Test Performance of College Students" (adjusted for group differences on SAT), he produces evidence that test results can be misleading if the threat of stereotype is introduced. Stereotype threat is an anxiety or concern in a situation where the person has the potential to confirm a negative stereotype about their social group. Steele defines it as "the social-psychological threat that arises when one is in a situation or doing something for which a negative stereotype about one's group applies" (Steele, 1997, p. 614). Steele gave the GRE (graduate school exam) to two groups that had been admitted to Stanford University, African Americans and Whites, but said nothing special about the test beforehand. The two groups were equal in intelligence. The assumption was that the test was real and that it would count. The African American group did not do as well as Whites. Steele then split the group into three subgroups; a stereotype threat group that were told that the test was a measure of their intelligence, a non-stereotype threat group that was told the test was a laboratory problem-solving task non-indicative of their intelligence, and a third condition who were told to judge the test on difficulty, but was non-indicative of their intelligence. The results were drastically different. This time the African-Americans in the non-stereotype threat treatment groups improved their scores a statistically significant amount (adjusted for previous SAT scores). "The brain cannot simultaneously worry about performance, and actually perform well" (Berube, 2014, p. 56). Another student stated that she was indeed a victim of the "stereotype threat" and was intimidated with math and science for this reason, and therefore since her teachers did not expect her to do well, she felt the pressure.

Most of the students were not looking forward to teaching science; only two students were looking forward to it, including the pre-engineering major. The rest were not. Five of the students were looking forward to teaching math, while two were not. Surprisingly, more preservice elementary teachers seem to be more comfortable with math than science. One of the students stated that her classes always held her back, since she seemed to be better at math then her classmates or groups she was placed in. She stated that most of her classmates were not on grade level and that her teachers didn't seem to be very good at math themselves.

All of the students said they were going to give it their best when it came their time to teach math and science in their own classrooms and were looking forward to learning more in the science for children class in order to do so. PBL has been successful in past science education courses (Thomas et al., 2013) in raising the science self-efficacy of preservice science teachers. Embedding science content in real-world problems makes science "real" for not only African American preservice teachers but for all teachers who are taught how to employ this pedagogy.

DISCUSSION

Dr. Berube's students for the most part discussed their unease with STEM subjects in general, and that many of them were not looking forward to teaching these subjects. This mirrors elementary teacher's attitudes across the nation (Kazempour, 2008; Mausner, 2011). It is for this reason that science and math need to be highlighted in teacher preparation programs, in order that future teachers, including African American and minorities of all creeds and cultures, feel ownership and that they can competently deliver quality science and math instruction, including PBL that embed real-world math and science problems into their daily lesson plans. This chapter focuses on African American preservice teachers and their attitudes, but all teachers in every elementary school in America have this important job: to insure that their students receive a quality math and science education.

APPENDIX

Preservice Science and Mathematics Education Qualitative Survey

Please answer each question as *honestly* as possible.

1. As a future elementary school teacher, are you looking forward to teaching science? Why or why not?
2. As a future elementary mathematics teacher, are you looking forward to teaching mathematics? Why or why not?
3. As a future secondary school teacher, are you looking forward to teaching science? Why or why not?
4. As a future secondary school teacher, are you looking forward to teaching mathematics? Why or why not?
5. Describe how you feel about science/math and why.
6. Explain how learning PBL has affected your feelings about teaching science or math.
7. As an African-American, have you faced obstacles that your White classmates did not have to face? If so, what are they?
8. How were you taught science and math as a child?
9. As an African American, what do you think you would do differently as a science/math teacher when you get your own classroom?

REFERENCES

American Association for the Advancement of Science. (1990). *Science for all Americans: Project 2061.* Retrieved from http://www.project2061.org/publications/sfaa/online/sfaatoc.htm

Appleton, K. (2003). How do beginning primary school teachers cope with science? Toward an understanding of science teaching practice. *Journal for Research in Science Teaching, 33*(1), 1–25.

Basso, R. (2012, March 2). *How STEM jobs are leading our future and why you should care* [Blog post]. Retrieved from http://www.openforum.com/articles/how-stem-jobs-are-leading-our-future-and-why-you-should-care.

Bell, R. L., Smetana, L., & Binns, I. (2005) Simplifying inquiry instruction. *The Science Teacher, 72,* 30–33.

Berkman, M. B., Pacheco, J. S., & Plutzer, E. (2008). Evolution and creationism in America's classrooms: A national portrait. *PLoSBiology, 6*(5), 920–924.

Berube, C. (2014). *STEM and the city: A report on STEM education in the great American urban public school system.* Charlotte, NC: Information Age.

Berube, C., Dash, S., & Thomas-Charles, C. (2019). *Nanoscience research modules for pre-service STEM teachers: Core nanoscience concepts as a vehicle in STEM education.* Charlotte, NC: Information Age.

Bracey, G. (2009). The Bracey Report on the Condition of Public Education, 2009. *Education Policy Research Unit.* https://files.eric.ed.gov/fulltext/ED507354.pdf

Carnegie Science Center. (2012, May 29). Careers of the future. *Pittsburgh Magazine.* Retrieved from http://www.pittsburghmagazine.com/Pittsburgh-Magazine/June-2012/STEM-Careers-of-the-Future-Pittsburgh/

Cohen, J. (1988). *Statistical power analysis for the behavioral sciences* (2nd ed.). New York, NY: Routledge.

Committee on Science, Space, and Technology House of Representatives. (2011). *STEM education in action: Learning today... Leading tomorrow.* Washington, DC: U.S. Government Printing Office.

Darnell, A., & Sherkat, D. (1997). The impact of protestant fundamentalism on educational attainment. *American Sociological Review, 62*(2), 306–316.

Deemer, S. (2004). Classroom goal orientation in high school classrooms: Revealing links between teacher beliefs and classroom environments. *Educational Research, 46*(1), 73–90.

Delisle, R. (1997). *How to use problem-based learning in the classroom.* Alexandria, VA: ASCD.

Ellison, C. G., & Musick, M. (1995). Conservative protestantism and public opinion toward science. *Review of Religious Research, 36*(3), 245–262.

Engler, J. (2012, June 15). STEM education is the key to U.S.'s economic future. *U.S. News and World Report.* Retrieved from http://www.usnews.com/opinion/articles/2012/06/15/stem-education-is-the-key-to-the-uss-economic-future.

Haberman, M. (1991). The pedagogy of poverty versus good teaching. *Phi Delta Kappan, 73*(4), 290–294.

Haberman, M. (1995). *Star teachers of children in poverty.* West Lafayette, IN: Kappa Delta Pi.

Haberman, M. (2005). *Star teachers: The ideology and best practice of effective teachers of diverse children and youth in poverty.* Houston, TX: The Haberman Educational Foundation.

Haberman, M., (2009). Room 26, Martin Haberman Foundation, Haberman Room 26 (video). *YouTube.* https://www.youtube.com/watch?v=rE0jVizkWcQ

Hiebert, J. (2003). What research says about the NCTM standards. In J. Kilpatrick, W. G. Martin, & D. Schifter (Eds.), *A research companion to principles and standards for school mathematics* (pp. 5–23). Reston, VA: National Council of Teachers of Mathematics.

Hmelo-Silver, C. (2004). Problem-based learning; What and how do students learn? *Educational Psychology Review, 16*(3), 235–266.

Kayne, E., (2013, June 13). Census: White majority in U.S. gone by 2043. *NBC News.*

Kazempour, M. (2008). *Exploring attitudes, beliefs, and self-efficacy of pre-service elementary teachers enrolled in a science method course and factors responsible for possible changes* (Doctoral dissertation). Indiana University, Bloomington, IN.

Kendricks, K., & Arment, A. (2010). *Adopting a K–12 family model with undergraduate research to enhance STEM persistence and achievement in underrepresented minority students.* Minneapolis: Institute for Mathematics and it's Applications, University of Minnesota.

Langdon, D., McKittrick, G., Beede, D., Khan, B., & Doms, M. (2012). *STEM: Good jobs now and for the future.* Washington, DC: U.S. Department of Commerce, Economics and Statistics Administration.

Lienesch, M. (2007). *In the beginning: Fundamentalism, the scopes trial, and the making of the antievolution movement.* Chapel Hill: University of North Carolina Press.

Locke, G., (2011, July 14). STEM jobs help america win the future. *The White House Blog.* Retrieved from http://www.whitehouse.gov/blog/2011/07/14/stem-jobs-help-america-win-future

Loftus, M. (2012). Brighter outlook: Community colleges find that faculty-student research projects help spot and develop STEM talent. *Prism, 21*(8), 36 – 39.

Lubienski, S. T. (2001, April). *A second look at mathematics achievement gaps: Intersections of race, class, and gender in NAEP data.* Paper presented at the American Educational Research Association, Seattle, WA.

Maltese, A. V., & Tai, R. H. (2010). Eyeballs in the fridge: Sources of early interest in science. *International Journal of Science Education, 32*(5), 669–685.

Manouchehri, A. (2004). Reforming high school mathematics: Considering the teachers' perspectives. *Action in Teacher Education, 11*(4), 98–123.

Mausner, J. (2011, October 26). Study: elementary school science education neglected. *The Daily Californian.* Retrieved from http://www.dailycal.org/2011/10/26/study-elementary-school-science-education-neglected/

McKinney, S., Bol, L., & Berube, C. (2010). Mathematics teaching with the stars. In B. Allison & B. Berghoff (Eds.), *Online yearbook of urban learning, teaching, and research* (pp. 36–50). Washington, DC: Urban Learning, Teaching, and Research Special Interest Group.

Morella, M. (2013, January31). Many high-schoolers giving up on STEM. *US News.* Retrieved from http://www.usnews.com/news/blogs/stem-education/2013/01/31/report-many-high-schoolers-giving-up-on-stem

National Council of Teachers of Mathematics. (2007). *Mathematics teaching today.* Reston, VA: Author.

National Council of Teachers of Mathematics. (2000). *Principles and standards for school mathematics* (NCTM, ed.). Reston, VA: Author.

National Research Council. (2007). *Taking science to school: Learning and teaching science in grades K–8.* Washington, DC: National Academy Press.

National Research Council. (2011). *A framework for K–12 science education: Practices, crosscutting concepts, and core ideas.* Washington, DC: National Academy Press.

Palmer, R., Ryan, D., Moore, J., III, & Hilton, A. (2010). A nation at risk: Increasing participation and persistence among African-American males to stimulate U.S. global competitiveness. *Journal of African-American Males in Education, 1*(2), 105–124.

Payton, F. (2004). Making STEM careers more accessible. *Black Issues in Higher Education, 21*(2), 90.

Pew Research Center's Religion & Public Life Project. (2013). Retrieved from https://www.pewforum.org/2016/07/13/2-religion-in-public-life

Sehgal, N., & Smith, G. (2009, January 30). A religious portrait of African-Americans. *Pew Research Center's Forum on Religion & Public Life.* http://www.pewforum.org/A-Religious-Portrait-of-African-Americans.aspx

Sherkat, D. E. (2011). Religion and scientific literacy in the United States. *Social Science Quarterly, 92*(5), 1134–1150.

Steele, C. M. (1997). A threat in the air: How stereotypes shape intellectual identity and performance. *American Psychologist, 52*(6), 613–629. https://doi.org/10.1037/0003-066X.52.6.613

Sterling, D. (2007). Modeling problem-based instruction: A health-science investigation put students in the role of epidemiologists. *Science and Children, 45*(4), 50–53.

Sterling, D., & Hargrove, D. (2012). Is your soil sick? *Science and Children, 49*(8), 51–55.

Sterling, D., Matkins, J. J., Frazier, W., & Logerwell, M. (2007). Science camp as a transformative experience for students, parents, and teachers in the urban setting. *School Science and Mathematics, 107*(4), 134–147.

Tarhan, L., & Acar, B. (2007). Problem-based learning in an eleventh grade chemistry class: "Factors affecting cell potential." *Research in Science & Technological Education, 25*(3), 351–369. https://doi.org/10.1080/02635140701535299

The Obama Education Plan: An Education Week Guide. (2009). San Francisco, CA: Jossey-Bass.

Thomas, K., Horne, P., Donnelly, S., & Berube, C. (2013). Infusing problem-based learning (PBL) into science methods courses across the state of Virginia. *The Journal of Mathematics and Science: Collaborative Explorations, 13*(1), 93–110.

Virginia Initiative for Science Teaching and Achievement. (2011). George Mason University. Retrieved from http://vista.gmu.edu/

ABOUT THE EDITORS

Beverly J. Irby is a professor, and associate dean of academic affairs at the College of Education and Human Development at Texas A&M University. Dr. Irby is also the director of the Educational Leadership Research Center. Her primary research interests center on issues of social responsibility, including bilingual and English-as-a-second-language education, science-infused literacy and literacy-infused science, administrative structures, curriculum, instructional strategies, and women's and girls' issues. She is the author of more than 200 refereed articles, chapters, books, and curricular materials for Spanish-speaking children. She is the series editor for *Research on Women and Education* (RWE). She has had in excess of $90,000,000 in grants. She was awarded in 2009, the Texas State University System—Regents Professor. Dr. Irby has extensive experiences working with undergraduate students in the past 25+ years, and many of these students are underrepresented including first-generation college students, ethnic and economically challenged students, and have obtained doctorates and received research/teaching awards under her mentorship. Dr. Irby is the editor of the *Mentoring and Tutoring: Partnership in Learning* journal.

Barbara Polnick is a full professor in the Department of Educational Leadership at Sam Houston State University, Huntsville, Texas. Her involvement in STEM, specifically mathematics, spans over 40 years. From high school mathematics teacher, mathematics and curriculum specialist, curriculum director and now professor at Sam Houston State University, she has focused much of her work on improving teaching and learning in mathematics, as it relates to gender, leadership, and early childhood. Her expertise lies in writing and evaluating grants, leading school improvement initiatives, and curriculum alignment. Author of 47 publications (peer-reviewed articles, book chapters, textbook), she has delivered over 60 national presentations. She holds an EdD in educational administration from Texas A&M University and a master's in reading from Sam Houston State University. She is past chair of the *Research on Women and Education* (RWE) AERA SIG, currently serving on the RWE executive committee, and recipient of the RWE Information Age Author Legacy Award. Dr. Polnick is an especially proud recipient of the Texas A&M University College of Education and Human Development Outstanding Alumni Award.

Julia Ballenger is a professor in the Department of Educational Leadership at A&M University-Commerce. Dr. Ballenger's research agenda includes mentoring, gender equity, standards of school-based leadership, women of color in STEM, leadership for social justice, and culturally relevant pedagogy. Dr. Ballenger is the author of 25 book chapters, 30 peer-reviewed articles, and co-editor of eight books. Dr. Ballenger can be reached at julia.ballenger@tamuc.edu

Nahed Abdelrahman, PhD, educational administration at the Department of Educational Administration and Human Resources. Dr. Abdelrahman is the coordinator of the Preparing Academic Leaders master's program ($2.57 million federal grant). Her research interests center on education policy and principal preparation. Dr. Abdelrahman is a recipient of Kottcamp Distinguished Dissertation Award of 2019 from the Learning and Teaching in Educational Leadership Sig at the American Educational Research Association (AERA). She also was selected as a Barbara Jackson Scholar from (2015–2017). Dr. Abdelrahman authored and co-authored more than 14 publications and more than 35 presentations in the annual meetings of prestigious conferences including AERA, UCEA, RWE, and NCPEA. Her email address is nrahman@tamu.edu

ABOUT THE CONTRIBUTORS

Clair Berube is assistant professor of education at Virginia Wesleyan University where she teaches courses in the Department of Education. Before becoming a professor, Dr. Berube taught middle school science in Norfolk Public Schools, where she won a teaching award. Dr. Berube has also won teaching awards at the university level. She has published several articles and books on education issues, including STEM, urban education, and social justice.

Erika C. Bullock is assistant professor of curriculum studies and mathematics education in the Department of Curriculum and Instruction at the University of Wisconsin-Madison. She historicizes issues and ideologies within mathematics education to examine how power operates within mathematics education to create and maintain inequities. Her work has been published in outlets including *Educational Studies, Review of Research in Education, The Journal of Education,* and *Teachers College Record.*

Solongo Chuluunbaatar is a PhD student at the University of Illinois at Chicago. She received a bachelor's degree in mathematics from Brigham Young University-Hawaii and a master's degree in mathematics education from Brigham Young University. She is interested in a role of language and communication in mathematics education and higher education.

Kyaien O. Conner is an assistant professor of mental health law and policy at the University of South Florida in the College of Behavioral and Community Sciences. Her research examines behavioral health disparities facing

Women of Color In STEM, pages 161–166
Copyright © 2021 by Information Age Publishing
161

racial and ethnic minorities. Her research has been funded by the National Institutes of Health and the Hartford Foundation. She can be reached at koconner@usf.edu

Alberto Esquinca is associate professor in the Department of Dual Language and English Learner Education at San Diego State University. His research interests include STEM literacy practices, particularly among emergent bilingual, Latinx, and transitional students.

Krystal A. Foxx is currently an adjunct instructor with two community colleges in North Carolina and the director of a STEAM initiative targeted towards promoting STEM/STEAM to middle and high school youth in her hometown. She continues to pursue her research agenda in areas such as community college leadership; student access, retention, and success; mentoring; STEM/STEAM education for underrepresented populations; and school-community partnerships.

Sonia Garcia is the senior director for the access and inclusion program in the College of Engineering at Texas A&M University. She joined the college in 2014. In this role, Garcia is responsible for the initiation, development, management, evaluation, and promotion of research informed and strategic comprehensive activities and programs for the recruitment and success of historically underrepresented minority students and underserved communities in engineering at the undergraduate and graduate levels. She has received many awards throughout her professional career, including the 2019 Texas A&M's Diversity Service Award, the 2008 President's Award for Academic Advising, and the 2017 Dr. Roberts M. Gates Inspiration Award Garcia received her BS in political science from the University of Massachusetts at Boston, her MS in human development from the University of Rhode Island, and her PhD in higher, adult, and lifelong education from Michigan State University. She speaks Spanish, English, and Italian fluently, and is well-versed in French.

Melva R. Grant, associate professor of mathematics education at Old Dominion University has been a mathematics educator for over 20 years. Her research is focused generally on broadening participation in STEM for underserved urban populations. Specifically, she leverages technology to develop mathematics teachers and teacher leaders. Dr. Grant also engages in critical theory research that reveals issues and promotes opportunities for improving equity and inclusion in education institutions.

Natasha Hillsman Johnson is an assistant professor in the Department of Teacher Education at the University of Toledo. Using a Black feminist theoretical framework, her current research utilizes cogenerative dialogue sessions among Black females to collectively identify critical issues in the freshman chemistry course and cogenerate solutions to improve the learning experience and academic outcome for Black female, undergraduate STEM students. The overarching goal of her scholarship is to increase interest, access, and achievement in the sciences for all students. She can be reached at natasha.johnson@utoledo.edu or nhillsmanjohnson@gmail.com

Patricia Horne Hastings is associate professor of education at Longwood University. Dr. Hastings' research interests focus on equity-based curriculum and instruction with particular emphasis on engaging traditionally marginalized populations in STEM. She places heavy emphasis on challenging privileged identities and systemic inequities in her work with preservice teachers. Prior to Longwood, Dr. Hastings was an assistant professor at Averett University where she implemented several engineering summer camps for local youth. Dr. Hastings is a former high school biology teacher who later found her passion for teacher development in with urban elementary teachers to foster inquiry-based science lessons in K–5 classrooms. She holds a Virginia teaching license with Meritorious Designation.

Sarah Hug is a research associate with the Alliance for Teaching, Learning, and Society (ATLAS) at the University of Colorado, Boulder. Her research interests include informal STEM learning, departmental culture and climate, and equity and access for underrepresented students in STEM fields. For the past decade, she has served as the external evaluator of the Computing Alliance of Hispanic-Serving Institutions, a consortium of computing departments seeking to broaden participation in computing to underserved populations.

Tonisha B. Lane is an assistant professor of higher education and student affairs at the University of South Florida. Her research areas are equity and inclusion in postsecondary education, underrepresented groups in STEM, and Black students and professionals in higher education. Her publications can be found in *CBE-Life Sciences Education and Equity & Excellence in Education*. She can be reached at tblane@usf.edu

Jacqueline Leonard is a professor in the School of Education at the University of Wyoming. Her research areas include computational thinking, culturally specific pedagogy, and teaching mathematics for social justice. As the 2018–2019 Fulbright Chair in STEM at the University of Calgary, she will conduct research on Indigenous students' computational thinking using computer modeling and game design. Leonard is author of 75 publications, author of two books, and co-editor of two books.

Liza Renee Lizcano graduated from Stanford University's Graduate School of Education in 2016, where she earned a doctorate in developmental and psychological sciences. She has served as an adjunct lecturer for online and in-seat courses in psychology, education, and statistics. In the fall of 2018, Dr. Lizcano joined the faculty at Colorado Christian University as an associate professor in the School of Education. Her research areas are Latin@ issues in education, STEM education, gender issues in education, and culturally responsive teaching practices. She can be reached at lizarenee@ alumni.stanford.edu

Sueanne McKinney is associate professor of education at Old Dominion University, and formerly assistant professor of mathematics education at Old Dominion University. Dr. McKinney has numerous publications concerning urban and mathematics education. She has created partnerships with several high-poverty urban public schools in the Norfolk Public School system, where she makes a huge difference in the daily lives of children. Dr. McKinney is currently working on several grants concerning STEM education in urban schools. Dr. McKinney taught middle school mathematics in Norfolk Public Schools, before becoming a college professor. She has won numerous teaching awards.

Erika Mein is associate professor of literacy/biliteracy education in the Department of Teacher Education at the University of Texas at El Paso. Her research interests include disciplinary literacies, engineering identities, and the postsecondary trajectories of primarily Latinx students. She can be reached at elmein2@utep.edu

Angelica Monarrez is a research associate in STEM education in the Department of Teacher Education at the University of Texas at El Paso (UTEP). Her research interests include mathematical knowledge, mathematical tasks, engineering identities, gender, and STEM education. She has published in various journals and edited books. She can be reached at amonarrez5@utep.edu

Melissa Soto is deputy director of the biology scholars program at the University of California, Berkeley. Her work as a scholar-practitioner includes broadening participation in higher education through research and practice in the areas of STEM undergraduate education, faculty development, STEM gender equity, and institutional transformation. She can be reached at m.soto@berkeley.edu

Joi Spencer is associate dean and associate professor of mathematics education in the School of Leadership and Education Sciences at the University of San Diego. Her work sits at the intersection of mathematics education, teacher education, and educational equity in urban and minoritized communities. Spencer is co-PI on the NSF grant, "Bridging the World of Work and Informal STEM Education." She chairs the editorial board for the *Journal for Research in Mathematics Education* and is the president of the California Association of Mathematics Teacher Educators.

Heather Thiry is a research associate with Ethnography & Evaluation Research (E&ER) at the University of Colorado, Boulder. Her research interests include diverse students' pathways in STEM undergraduate majors, the impact of out-of-class experiences on recruitment and retention in STEM fields, and the development of STEM identity among students from underrepresented populations. She is the author of numerous publications and book chapters, as well as a co-author of the forthcoming book, *Talking About Leaving Revisited* (Springer Nature Switzerland AG, 2019). She also recently served on a National Academy of Sciences committee, which produced the report, *Undergraduate Research Experiences for STEM Students: Success, Challenges, and Opportunities.* She can reached at heather.thiry@colorado.edu

Virginia C. Tickles is an aerospace engineer in Huntsville, AL and a member of the Sisters of the Academy (SOTA) Institute (www.sistersoftheacademy.org). Her research focus is anchored in the experiences of Black women, particularly in the areas of mentoring, leadership, and/or STEM engagement. She is passionate about supporting STEM outreach and education opportunities in an effort to share her experiences with others seeking STEM careers. She can be reached at vctickles@gmail.com

Elsa Villa is a research assistant professor at The University of Texas at El Paso (UTEP) sharing her appointment between the UTEP Office of Research and Sponsored Projects and the UTEP College of Education where she is director of the Center for Education Research and Policy Studies. With teacher certification in the State of Texas for secondary mathematics and science, Villa has taught at numerous levels: Grades 7 through 12, community college, and university in the disciplines of mathematics, science, education, engineering, and computer science. Villa has led and co-led numerous STEM grants from corporate foundations and state and federal agencies. She recently led an NSF-funded grant investigating identity and agency of undergraduate Latina engineering and computer science students. Currently, Villa leads an interdisciplinary project funded by the U.S. Department of Education to increase success of STEM majors in precalculus. With publications in various refereed journals and edited books, her research interests include communities of practice, gender, STEM teacher education, transformative learning, and identity.

Erica N. Walker is Clifford Brewster Upton professor of mathematics education and chairperson of the Department of Mathematics, Science, and

Technology at Teachers College, Columbia University. She is also the director of the Institute for Urban and Minority Education at TC. An award-winning former public high school mathematics teacher from Atlanta, Georgia, she earned her doctorate in education from Harvard University. Her research focuses on the social and cultural factors as well as educational policies and practices that facilitate mathematics engagement, learning, and performance, especially for underserved students. Recognized by the National Association of Mathematicians and the Association for Women in Mathematics for her scholarship and practice, she collaborates with teachers, schools, districts, organizations, and media outlets to promote mathematics excellence and equity for young people. Her work has been published in journals such as the *American Education Research Journal, Journal for Research in Mathematics Education, Educational Leadership,* and the *Urban Review.* Professor Walker serves on several editorial boards and is the author of two books: *Building Mathematics Learning Communities: Improving Outcomes in Urban High Schools* (published by Teachers College Press in 2012) and *Beyond Banneker: Black Mathematicians and the Paths to Excellence,* published by SUNY Press in 2014.

Rosalía Chávez Zárate is currently a postdoctoral fellow at the Department of Sociology and Education at the Teachers College at Columbia University. Her mixed-methods research focuses on higher education policy, retaining underrepresented students in higher education, and improving equity in STEM (science, technology, engineering, and mathematics) fields. She can be reached at rosaliaczarate@gmail.com